CW00765371

HARLAND & WOLFF

Designs from the Shipbuilding Empire

"WAIPARA"

LENGTH OF KEEL AND FORERAKE
BEAM
DEPTH OF HOLD
TONNAGE NETT
ENGINES 10 H.P. NOM. EACH PAIR.
SCALE 6 M. 1 FOOT

HARLAND & WOLFF
Designs from the Shipbuilding Empire

Tom McCluskie

CONWAY
MARITIME PRESS

This edition first published in Great Britain in 1998 by
Conway Maritime Press
a division of Batsford Communications PLC
583 Fulham Road
London SW6 5BY
http://www.batsford.com

British Library Cataloguing in Publication Data
A record for this title is available on request from the
British Library

© 1998 PRC Publishing Ltd

All rights reserved. No part of this publication may
be reproduced, stored in a retrieval system,
or transmitted in any form or by any means, electronic,
mechanical, photocopying, recording, or otherwise,
without the prior written permission of the Publisher
and copyright holders.

ISBN 0 85177 767 8

Printed and bound in Singapore

CONTENTS

INTRODUCTION

The city and port of Belfast has been associated with the building of ships for over three hundred years, with the first recorded vessels being registered in 1663. The River Lagan, which flows through the heart of Belfast, provided the foundation for the steady rise in prosperity of the city, allowing merchants ready access to sea-going vessels. The establishment of this commercial trade led naturally to the provision of vessel repair and service facilities which would evolve into shipbuilding works and, eventually, the formation of the massive Harland & Wolff shipbuilding complex of today. However, there were to be several false starts and many tribulations along the way.

Today the River Lagan is a clean and relatively straight waterway far removed from its original course which meandered its narrow and twisting course through the city in the eighteenth century. At that time the ever-increasing use of the river for commerce prompted the establishment of the Belfast Harbour Commissioners in 1785, under the official and grandiose title of 'The Corporation for Preserving and Improving the Port and Harbour of Belfast'. This august body of men, comprising mostly merchants and traders, immediately set in motion a programme of improvements to the quays along the river banks as well as straightening and widening the river itself in several places by means of two straight cuts towards the mouth of Belfast Lough. The construction work involved the excavation and dumping of millions of tons of soil at the mouth of the river along the eastern side of the shoreline. The massive amount of material deposited eventually formed an island which would, in time, be named Queen's Island in honour of Queen Victoria, who was to officially open the newly reconstructed port facilities in August 1849.

This feverish activity had not gone unnoticed and the improvements soon attracted the attention of William Ritchie, an established shipbuilder from Saltcoats in Scotland. Ritchie had visited Belfast in 1791 and had been impressed by the the new port facilities, offering as they did the potential for expansion in the shipbuilding business. Approaching the Harbour Commissioners with a proposal to establish a shipyard, Ritchie was delighted to be offered, in return for his investment, a new docking platform on which vessels could be beached for cleaning and repair. The arrival of William Ritchie and his company in Belfast laid the foundations of a shipbuilding tradition which would result, some sixty years later, in the ambition of Edward Harland to develop his new venture, Harland & Wolff, into the greatest shipbuilding company in the world.

Edward Harland was born in May 1831, in Scarborough, Yorkshire, the sixth child of Dr. William Harland, a successful and well-respected medical practitioner. Dr. Harland had also established something of a reputation as an inventor, having designed and patented a steam carriage in 1827. From a very young age, Edward also displayed a talent for engineering and, by his own admission, neglected his academic studies, preferring to watch engineers at work. This is not, perhaps, surprising – his father was a close personal friend of the famous scientist and engineer George Stephenson.

While his father hoped that Edward would eventually tire of his obsession and return to his studies as a barrister, Edward was just as determined to become a professional engineer and in 1846, having finished his grammar school studies, accepted an apprenticeship with Robert Stephenson & Company of Newcastle. During his apprenticeship Edward became deeply interested in the design of ships and the practicalities of shipbuilding. A particular preoccupation he had at this time was the huge death toll among seafarers and in the summer of 1850, he developed a new design for a lifeboat which would have a propeller at each end. However, to his great disappointment, the idea was rejected. Undeterred, he determined to continue with his ideas for sea-going vessels and returned to his studies with renewed vigour.

As his apprenticeship progressed, Edward had become friendly with Gustav Christian Schwabe, a wealthy merchant born in Hamburg in 1813. Gustav's eldest sister, Fanny, was married to her brother's best friend, Moritz Wolff, with whom she had two sons – Gustav Wilhelm, born in 1834, and George Moritz Otto, born in 1840.

Gustav Wolff had arranged to leave home at fourteen to live with his uncle, Gustav Schwabe, in Liverpool where he was to attend Liverpool college to study engineering and take up an apprenticeship with Joseph Whitworth & Company of Manchester. The young Gustav quickly established a reputation as an excellent engineer and was honoured to represent Whitworth & Co. at the Paris engineering exhibition in 1855. In 1856, ever keen to improve his engineering skills, Gustav joined B. Goodfellows Limited of Hyde as a draughtsman. However, this post was to be short-lived as later in the same year he accepted a position with the Belfast shipbuilders Robert Hickson & Company as a junior manager (such positions were only provided to the sons of wealthy parents wishing to learn a business in which they hoped eventually to become directors). Gustav's move to Belfast resulted in his working with Edward Harland, whom he had known for a long time as a friend of his father.

Edward Harland himself had arrived in Belfast during the summer of 1854 to take up the appointment of shipyard manager to Robert Hickson & Company. Upon his arrival Edward had immediately taken charge of the only vessel under construction, the *Khersonese*, which was already far behind schedule for completion. Edward set about improvements in the working methods to recover as much of the lost time as possible, although his enthusiasm was not universally welcomed by the workforce. To his horror he found that Hickson had been paying wages far above the usual rate and had accepted shoddy and inferior craftsmanship. Edward immediately slashed the wages and introduced a system of work inspection whereby inferior work was rejected and repaired at the craftsman's own expense. To improve discipline and safety further he prohibited smoking in the workplace and insisted that no employee was to stand with his hands in his pockets for any reason. Not surprisingly these austere measures resulted in the workers going on strike. Edward responded by sacking the entire workforce and replacing them with labour recruited from Scotland. These shock tactics had the desired effect and, after a short while, the striking workers returned and accepted their new terms and conditions.

Unknown to the workers however, Edward Harland was facing difficulties of a much more serious nature. In the spring of 1855, the Ulster Banking Company, long concerned at the fiscal performance of Hickson's operations, finally lost patience and foreclosed on all outstanding business loans. This disastrous state of affairs resulted in Edward having to fund the daily operating costs from his own pocket, while attempting to reach some sort of accommodation with the yard's creditors. Struggling to keep the yard in operation, Edward Harland found himself with some unexpected help. Thomas Toward & Company was a shipbuilding company on the Tyne and had employed Edward for a year in 1853. Following the death of the founder, Thomas Toward, in 1855, the head foreman, William Houston, and a large number of craftsmen moved to Belfast to help complete the *Khersonese*. The influx of this skilled labour increased production time and the quality of work greatly, with the result that Edward gained a breathing space to sort out the financial mess that he had inherited from Hickson.

To assist in the reconstruction of the company Edward appointed Gustav Wolff as his personal assistant in 1857 and together the two friends proceeded to assemble a rescue package for the company. Despite many difficulties and much pressure from creditors, on 21 September, 1858, Hickson offered Edward Harland the opportunity to purchase his entire interest in the shipyard for £5,000. Edward turned to his old friend, and Wolff's uncle, Gustav Schwabe for advice. With Schwabe's financial support and encouragement, Edward Harland purchased the shipbuilding enterprise of Robert Hickson on 1 November, 1858, and immediately changed the name to Edward James Harland & Company.

Edward progressed his shipbuilding operations by disposing of the original site of the Hickson yard and taking out a lease on the new Queen's Island. This allowed him to lay out a yard that was to his own requirements and the greater land area available also afforded him the freedom for further expansion as necessary. Edward Harland, now in control of his own destiny, rapidly expanded his shipbuilding operations and, simultaneously, his reputation for quality and reliability. Gustav Wolff, who had been appointed by Edward as chief draughtsman in the new company, had performed sterling service in reorganising the drawing offices and had also worked closely with Edward on the development of new and innovative vessel designs. In Wolff, Edward found a kindred spirit who shared his dreams and ideas – particularly those concerning the development of modern, iron steam ships – and it was no surprise when, on 11 April, 1861, the two friends formally entered into partnership by establishing the shipbuilding and engineering company of Harland & Wolff Limited.

With the official formation of the partnership between Edward Harland and Gustav Wolff, the renowned shipbuilding company of Harland & Wolff came into being on 1 January, 1862, and was soon to lead the world with its introduction of innovative and technologically advanced designs for ships of all types. The reputation gained by the company for excellence in vessel design and quality of construction has been maintained up to and including the present day some 137 years later. An illustration of this may be found in the price paid for second-hand vessels built by the company, or the residual value of the vessels when finally going for scrap. Vessels built by Harland & Wolff routinely attract the highest resale and scrap values of comparable vessels, chiefly because their inherent strength and durability makes them exceedingly difficult to destroy.

After Hickson had sold his interest in the shipyard to the young Harland, Edward quickly set about the onerous task of convincing the shipowners of the day to consider his designs. Harland realised however, that his first task would be to establish his credentials as a shipbuilder of quality and reliability by producing sturdy vessels to tried and trusted traditional designs. Over several years he had, during his time with Hicksons, established a reputation with John Bibby, the Liverpool shipowner, and it was from Bibby that Edward Harland received his first shipbuilding orders.

In April 1858, John Bibby signed a contract with Edward Harland for the construction of three vessels of approximately 1,500 tons each; to be named *Venetian, Sicilian & Syrian*. These three were each fitted with an auxiliary steam engine although, as the horse power was less than the sail area, they were classed as sailing ships. Such was Bibby's personal faith in Harland's abilities in vessel design that he agreed to allow Edward to construct these new vessels to his new design of hull which was a radical departure from the normal shape of short length on a wide beam. Harland's unique design adopted a long narrow hull shape which produced a greater tonnage capacity without the corresponding increase in vessel weight or the need for the greater power of an increased sail area.

This design proved to be successful in service, producing greater voyage speeds than ever before achieved as well as increased stability in heavy seas. Consequently, John Bibby returned to Harland for a further series of sixteen vessels. Innovative as Edward's designs were, they were still regarded with caution by other shipowners less progressive than Bibby, with the result that while Edward continued to refine and develop his ideas he was also engaged in building ships to more traditional specifications, such as his fifth vessel *Jane Porter*.

While sailing vessels were the accepted mode of vessel propulsion in the 1860s, the development of the steam engine as a method of powering a vessel was becoming a consideration. Edward Harland, himself a fervent supporter of this new technology, found it difficult to combine the pressures of running what was quickly becoming a very successful shipbuilding company with the development of marine steam engines. However, thanks to his new partner, they could consequently offer a significant contribution to the introduction of steam propulsion.

The adoption of steam as a method of powering a vessel was not quite so enthusiastically welcomed by the shipowners as the partners would have hoped. Their ideas, while being generally accepted as feasible, were for the most part untried and, being naturally conservative in their approach to all things new, shipowners preferred the 'wait and see' attitude to such new technology. It again fell to John Bibby to come to the rescue of the partners in agreeing to try a steam engine as the primary method of propulsion in the two new vessels that he intended to order from Harland & Wolff. Not entirely convinced by the partners' presentation and assurances, he also insisted that the conventional arrangement of sails be provided, just in case. The result was the appearance, in 1861, of the striking *Grecian* and *Italian* – each embodying all that was new and innovative in vessel design and construction. Close observation of the drawings will reveal once again the quality and attention to detail evident in the production of these plans; from the sectional view, through the engine and boiler room, with the water tanks and coal bunkers minutely detailed, to the internal structural arrangement of the hull. The revolutionary long slim hull form, which became known colloquially as the 'Bibby coffin' or more correctly and as preferred by Edward Harland, the 'Belfast Bottom', is also clearly evident. The grace and power of these vessels enhanced the reputation of Harland & Wolff throughout the world as innovative and progressive shipbuilders. Shipowners soon began to follow the example set by John Bibby and approach Harland & Wolff for new and better designs of vessels. The following pages provide graphic illustrations of the rapid development in Edward Harland's radical new concepts in ship design as well as illustrations of some of the most beautiful and graceful vessels ever to cross the world's oceans. Quality, craftsmanship and attention to detail are all prevalent in these drawings which could be regarded as works of art – much like the vessels themselves.

The design of merchant and naval vessels of all types has progressed beyond all recognition from those of the 1860s but the craftsmanship and pride in the achievement of producing a working vessel remains very much the same in the hearts of shipbuilders today as it did all those years ago. Similarly, the drawings produced by the draughtsmen and women which turn the designer's concept into a reality have also radically changed. In the modern shipyard, CAD/CAM and other computer-based tools have replaced much of the manual draughting and the complex calculations necessary to produce the construction drawings. Photocopiers and other reproductive devices have also removed the need for the vast armies of tracers who were required to produce copies of the original drawings for issue to the shipyard departments or the vessel owner.

Such drawings, many reproduced for the first time in this book, are indicative of that bygone age and reflect the attention to detail and craftsmanship so evident in the standard of work produced; for example each drawing is hand-coloured to reflect the various aspects of the vessel arrangement. These actual construction drawings are neither simply an attractive illustration of the type and appearance of a vessel, nor used for a purely decorative purpose in some grand shipping office; rather, they were of vital importance to the ship's master and officers in safely calculating the cargo stowage requirements. One copy of the drawing would be provided to the vessel's master, who would have had it carefully framed for protection and usually located in his cabin. From careful study of the drawing, the disposition of cargo according to weight or bulk and the requirement for ballast, if any, would have been calculated and the cargo loaded accordingly. The safety of a vessel at sea was the prime consideration to the mariners of that time, as indeed it remains today. However, modern vessels are equipped with an array of computer systems and equipment which produce the cargo loading plan in an instant and monitor the stresses on the hull to ensure that the cargo weight is correctly distributed and no dangerous conditions exist which could imperil the vessel. This is a far cry indeed from the solitary master with his copy of these drawings performing the complex calculations necessary to ensure the safety of his vessel.

The partnership of Edward James Harland and Gustav Wilhelm Wolff changed the face of shipbuilding globally: as the history of the company reflects, they were indeed 'Shipbuilders to the World'. At the height of their operations, Harland & Wolff had several shipyards in such diverse locations as Liverpool, Glasgow and London and directly employed some 65,000 people with perhaps five times as many working indirectly through sub contractors and suppliers. Recognised throughout shipowning circles as innovative shipbuilders they produced such instantly recognisable and beautiful vessels as *Titanic* and *Canberra*, vessels known and recognised throughout the world by ship enthusiasts and the layman alike. This book of the early designs provides a fascinating insight into the complexity and beauty of shipbuilding and the pride and craftsmanship that went into the construction of 'A Belfast Boat', as they were affectionately referred to by the workforce. Hard men working in a hard industry, these employees nevertheless experienced a tremendous sense of pride and achievement when a completed vessel departed her place of birth for the oceans of the world. Similarly, the sudden loss of a vessel – such as that of the R.M.S. *Titanic* was felt as deeply as a personal tragedy. Such was the depth of emotion and pride engendered in the art of shipbuilding and which can only truly be appreciated by those who have dedicated their lives to this industry. Hopefully, this volume of early designs will provide an insight into the unique and very special world of the shipbuilder and their craft.

Jane Porter

"JANE PORTER"

RIGGING PLAN
of
Nº 5

LENGTH of KEEL and FORERAKE = 200 FT.
BREADTH of BEAM = 32 FT.
DEPTH of HOLD = 21½ FT
TONNAGE = 99⁹⁄₉₅ BM.

DO: (actual) = 1005 ⁶⁄₉₅ BM.

Scale ½ = 1 foot
1860

Launched 1 September 1860	**Owner** James P Corry & Co, Belfast
Delivered 15 September 1860	**Gross Tonnage** 952 Tons
Yard Number 5	

The *Jane Porter* was the first iron vessel owned by the well renowned company of J P Corry & Company, Belfast, which is still in operation today as sawmill owners and timber merchants. In 1860, however, the Corry company had diverse business interests, principally in shipping and general merchants.

The Corry family were the owners of several vessels, all of which had the prefix 'Star' to their name. However, the founder of the company, James P Corry Senior, decided to name his first venture into the world of iron ships *Jane Porter* in honour of his mother.

The *Jane Porter* was designed as a sailing vessel – in 1860 the advent of steam power as a method of propulsion was very much in its infancy and accordingly much distrusted by shipowners who, being conservative in their approach to most things, preferred to continue their reliance on wind power. Edward Harland had for many years been a champion of steam as a motive power and had learned much from his father, Dr William Harland, who had designed and patented a steam-powered carriage in 1827.

Edward Harland was to find that his enthusiasm for steam was not understood or appreciated in the shipping world at that time; however, he did achieve a notable success with his revolutionary hull design. For several years he had been concerned at the frequent loss of sailing ships and the resultant terrible toll taken on human life of the unfortunate men who crewed these vessels. Appalled by these tragedies he turned his attention to the design of sailing vessels and how they could be improved: the result can be seen in the hull form of the *Jane Porter*.

The *Jane Porter* was one of the first vessels to be constructed using Edward Harland's new design incorporating a new type of iron deck which had the internal spaces between the frames filled with cement rather than the traditional wooden wedges or chocks. The deck itself was also covered with cement and tiles, providing an immensely strong and watertight construction.

Despite this tremendous leap forward in safety with the consequent reliability in vessel operation the shipowners still steadfastly provided only the minimal comforts in respect of the crews. Close observation of the deck plans will discover that the crew accommodation was provided in a simple deckhouse almost amidships and under the main deck at the after end. The only concession to luxury was a bath provided for the exclusive use of the vessel's master.

The cargo carried would have been of a general nature ranging from fine silks and china from the Far East to quarry stone and wool from the United Kingdom. Cargo was obtained on a 'where available' basis which resulted in the vessel having no specific route, giving rise to the modern idiom of the 'tramp' vessel navigating the globe in search of a profitable cargo. Accordingly, it was not unusual for the crews of these vessels to be away from home for several years at a time.

Jane Porter

"JANE PORTER"

RIGGING PLAN
of
N° 5

LENGTH of KEEL and a FORERAKE = 200. FT.
BREADTH of BEAM   = 32. FT.
DEPTH of HOLD   = 21½ FT
TONNAGE   = 990 BM.

DO: (actual)   = 1005 BM.

Scale ½" = 1 foot
1860

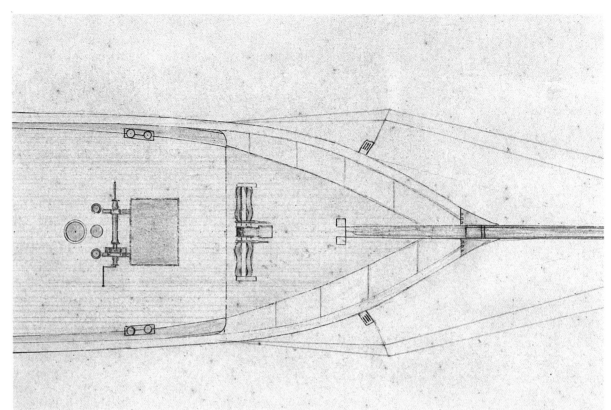

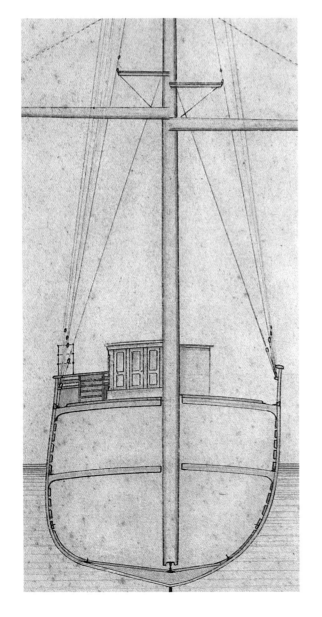

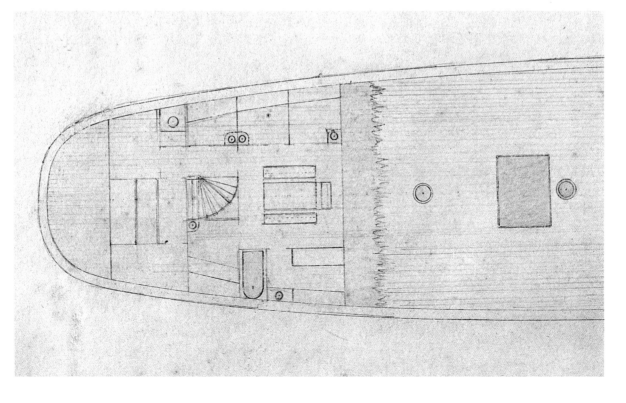

10

Jane Porter

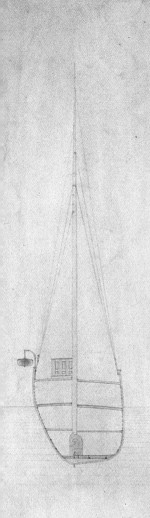

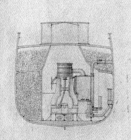
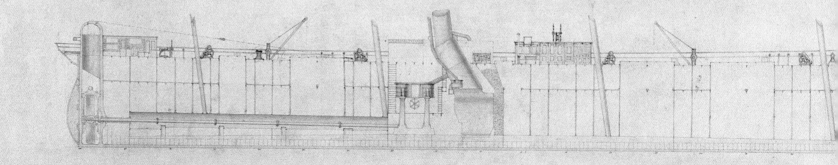

THE
GRECIAN AND ITALIAN.

Length of Keel & Forerake   310 0
Breadth of Beam   34 0
Depth of Hold from top of Floor   23 0
Builders Tonnage   1700 tons
Register Tonnage   1000

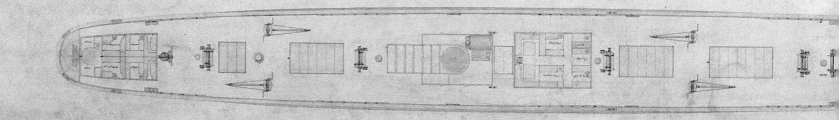

SCALE. ½ INCH TO 1 FOOT.

Grecian & Italian

	Grecian	Italian
Launched	12 January 1861	27 March 1861
Delivered	30 January 1861	13 April 1861
Yard Number	7	8
Owner	John Bibby Sons & Co, Liverpool (both)	
Gross Tonnage	1,854	1,859

The completion of *Grecian* and *Italian* marked the start of what was to prove to be a long association between the Bibby Line and Harland & Wolff. John Bibby had provided the fledgling company with its very first order, the sailing vessel *Venetian* which was completed on 14 August 1859. The vessel was a resounding success much to the delight of Bibby who had, after all, been persuaded to place a tremendous amount of faith in what at the time was an unestablished company. This trust was not exactly without foundation as Edward Harland had since 1850 been engaged by John Bibby to advise the company on the switch from sailing ships to steam propulsion. In the event, so impressed was John Bibby with the quality of construction and performance of the *Venetian* that he immediately ordered a further series of six vessels the first of which were to be the *Grecian* and *Italian*.

The placement of these orders provided Edward Harland with the opportunity to put into practice his designs for improved hull forms which he had developed during his time as chief draughtsman with J&G Thompson. Edward had developed a hull form that was unlike any of the day in that it provided for greater cargo capacity and passenger accommodation by constructing the vessels with an increased hull length without any corresponding increase in beam or width. In the case of *Grecian* and *Italian* this resulted in a length of 310 feet on a beam of thirty-four feet and an internal hold depth of twenty-four feet nine inches. This long and slender shape was of immense strength due to the adoption of Harland's patent iron deck, used for the first time on the *Jane Porter*, which produced a hull of a box girder design. Such were the fine lines and slender shape of their hulls, that the vessels quickly became known throughout shipping circles rather unfairly as the 'Bibby coffins'. Edward Harland no doubt preferred to refer to them by the official name which was the 'Belfast bottom' as they possessed a flat bottom allied to a square bilge.

The rigging employed in the design of the vessels was also unusual in its arrangement in that pole masts were fitted with a fore and aft sail rig providing a balanced and graceful profile. Steam winches were provided for cargo handling operations with the result that the crew numbers could be reduced. While steam was intended to be the main source of motive power, provided by an improved Halls Surface Condenser, the addition of sails provided an alternative and trusted method of propulsion. The Halls engine used sea water to condense the waste steam from the engine cylinders and preserved the pure water produced from the condensed steam for domestic use. This method provided enormous savings on fuel costs and repairs due to salt water corrosion.

Grecian went missing in 1873 and *Italian* was lost off Finisterre in 1869.

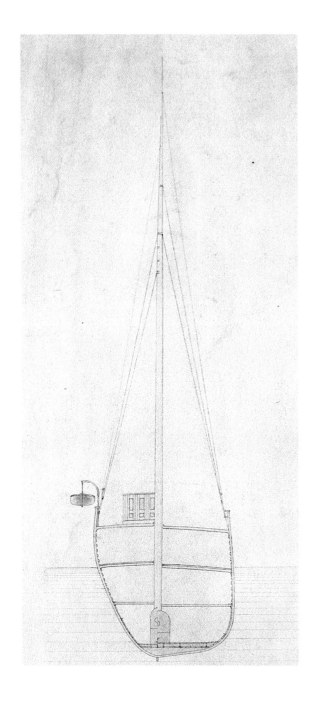

THE
GRECIAN AND ITALIAN.

	n. o
Length of Keel & Forerake	310. 0
Breadth of Beam	34. 0
Depth of Hold from top of Floor	25. 0
Builder's Tonnage	1700 tons
Register Tonnage	1551

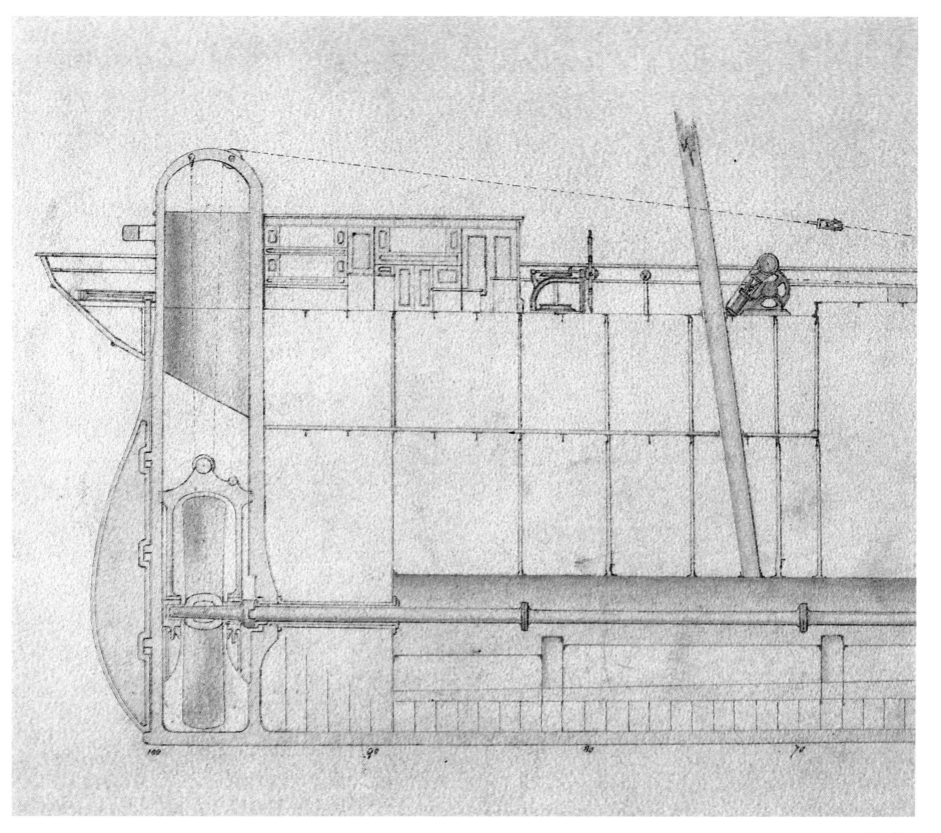

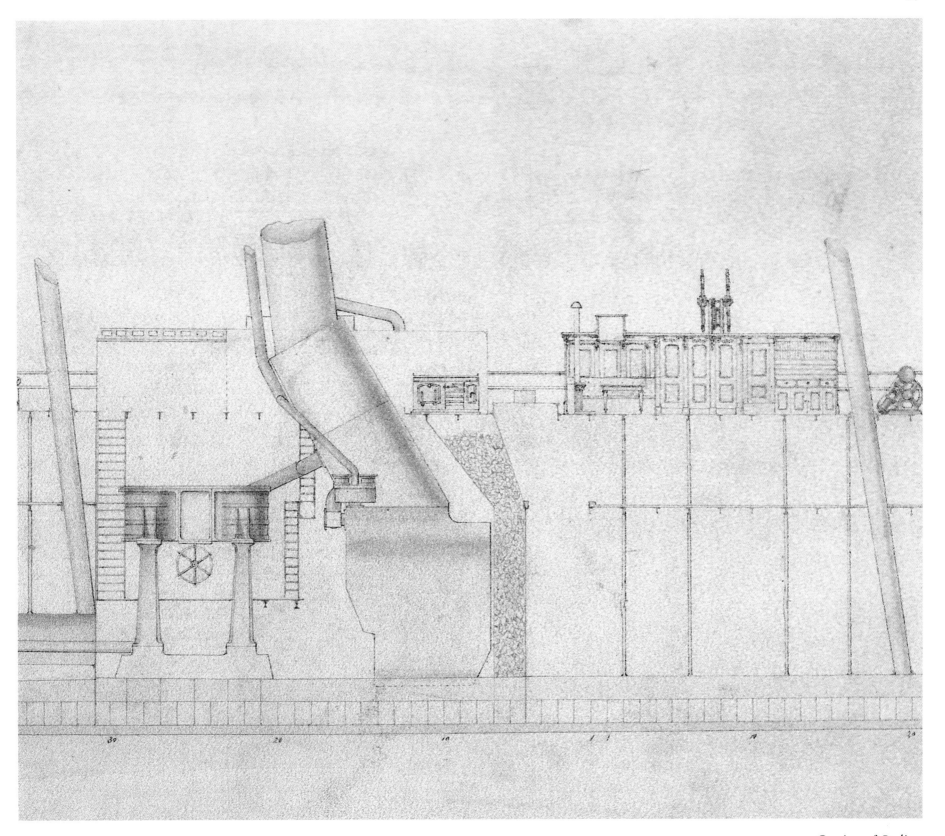

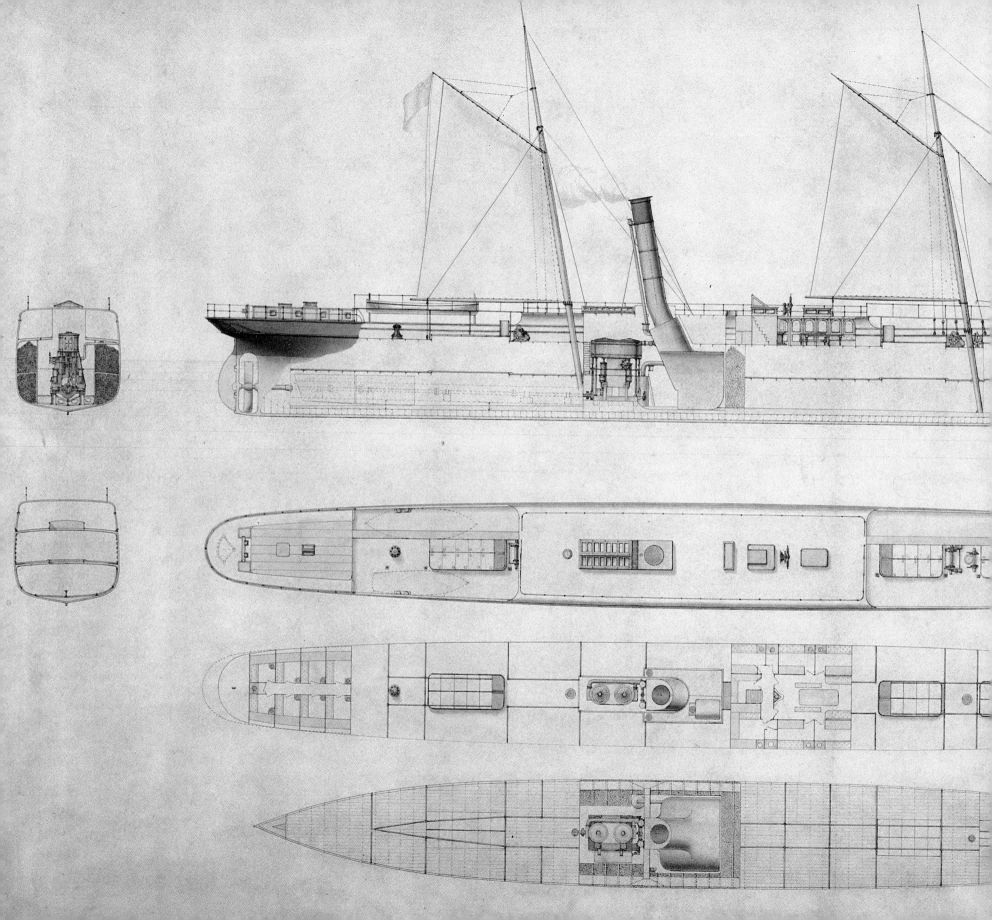

Castilian & Catalonian

	Castilian	*Catalonian*
Launched	10 May 1862	22 July 1862
Delivered	15 July 1862	2 August 1862
Yard Number	14	15
Owner	John Bibby Sons & Co, Liverpool	
Gross Tonnage	607	607

The construction of the *Castilian* and *Catalonian* marked the universal acceptance of the 'Belfast bottom' design which was now widely regarded as the optimum hull form. The introduction of these two vessels, which were the first to be specifically designed for a particular service route, signalled a progressive move to purpose-designed vessels as opposed to a general utilitarian type.

Bibby had recently secured a lucrative contract serving several Spanish ports from the United Kingdom on a regular basis, such a contract then being known as a 'liner service' although it had very little, if anything, to do with a passenger service. In essence, the service comprised the carriage of general goods in bulk or in bail condition and would be of varying tonnage. The demands of this type of operation meant that the vessels currently in service within the Bibby fleet were too large to enter the smaller ports and, with their large cargo capacity, were consequently uneconomical to operate. The soloution was the introduction of a scaled down version of the successful design already in service which became known as the 'baby Bibby'.

The introduction of these new vessels also marked a further advancement in ship design, and in particular engine technology and reliability. While the basic condenser design of engine was still employed, it had been much improved over the preceeding twelve months with the result that power output and reliability had been increased by approximately fifty percent. This increased performance allowed a reduction in the number of sails thought necessary, and accordingly the number of masts was reduced to two with a corresponding reduction in sail area. However, the major advantage from this increased power was the greater flexibility experienced when manoeuvring the vessel in port to and from the quayside.

The opportunity was also taken here to increase the standard of facilities and accommodation provided for the crew. As previously, the master and officers were granted spacious accommodation in a separate deckhouse forward of the funnel; however, all officers were now provided with individual cabins – something only previously enjoyed by the master. The crew was likewise provided for with twin cabins located in a deckhouse at the after end for the senior crew members such as the coxwain and bosun. The ordinary seamen enjoyed a spacious living accommodation under the main deck at the forward end. This arrangement was necessary to leave the forward end of the vessel clear for the provision of the mooring and anchor arrangements: it would be some time before the adoption of tiered deckhouses would be introduced for crew accommodation.

Catalonian would serve until her loss in 1863; *Castilian* had a much longer life and was converted to a lighter in Italy in 1915.

20

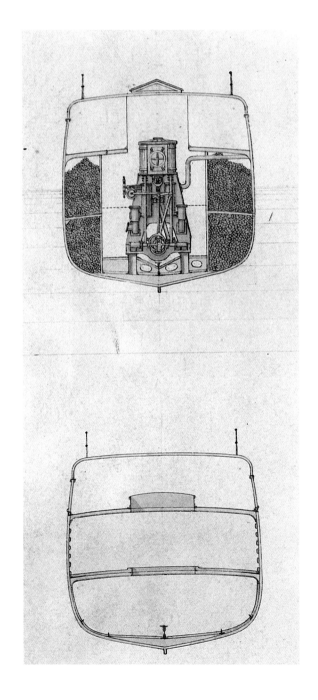

"CASTILIAN" AND "CATALONIAN."

	Feet	ins
LENGTH OF KEEL AND FORERAKE	240	0
BREADTH OF BEAM	24	0
DEPTH OF HOLD	15	8

SCALE 12 FEET = 1 INCH.

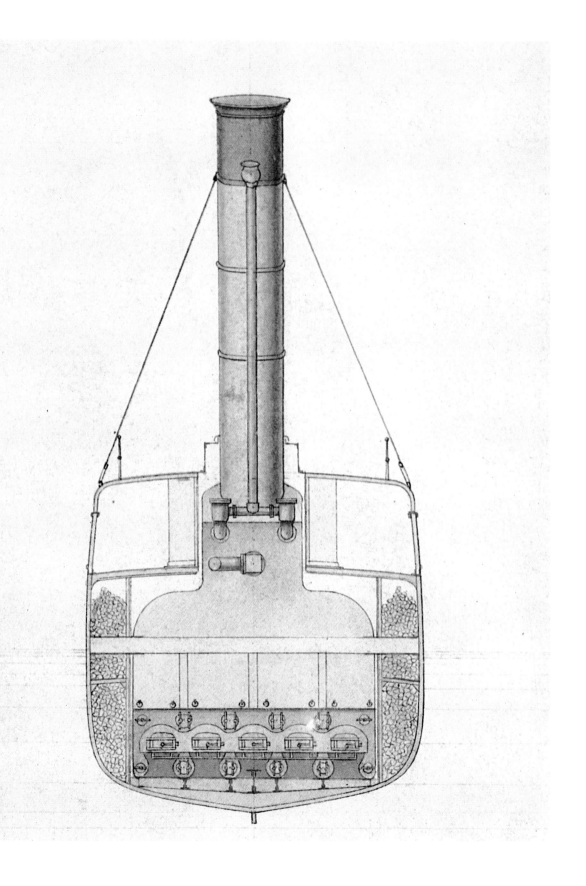

Castilian & Catalonian

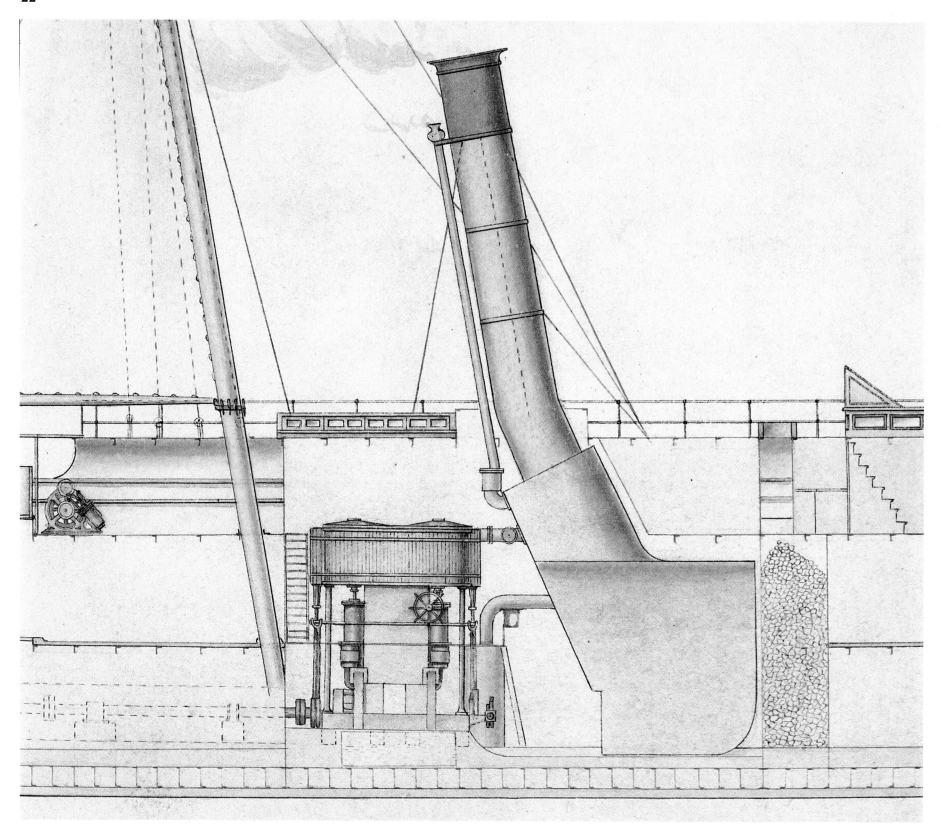

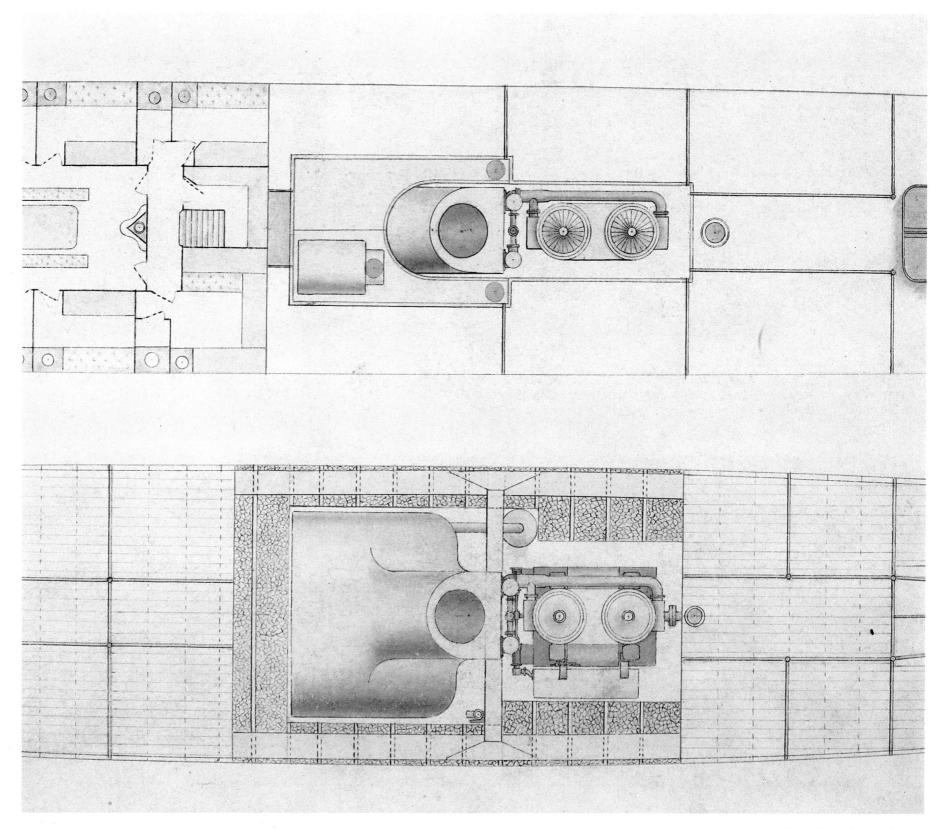

Castilian & Catalonian

Worrall

Launched 2 December 1862	**Owner** Mr James Worrall
Delivered 24 December 1862	**Gross Tonnage** 484
Yard Number 18	

The completion of the *Worrall* on Christmas eve 1862 marked Edward Harland's entry into the world of shipowning on his own account. He had agreed to the construction of this classic sailing vessel in partnership with the principal owner, local merchant James Worrall, who would oversee the operation and manning of the vessel. In return, Harland would reduce the building cost for the vessel in direct proportion to the number of shares he would hold. The common arrangement among shipowning partners was that a vessel would be divided into sixty-four equal parts with each share representing one sixty-fourth of the total vessel value. Time and mystery surround why this quaint arrangement for partnership should be established but what is known is that Edward Harland retained an interest in the vessel of twenty-two sixty-fourths which on average paid him a financial dividend of £1,900 per annum. Harland eventually disposed of his share interest in the vessel in 1883.

The *Worrall* was principally designed as a short sea trader operating to the continental European ports and throughout the Mediterranean. In this she was immensely successful, as is evidenced by the return on investment enjoyed by Harland even as the era of sailing ships as a means of transportation was drawing to a close. The spartan conditions provided for the crew bore little regard to their comfort and well being, with accommodation provided for everyone on board, including the master, in cramped quarters below the main deck at the aft end. Immediately above this was the solitary steering position which was connected directly to the rudder. No mechanical assistance was provided and conning or steering was dependant on brute force. The fact that the steering position was located so far aft only served to complicate further an already difficult task, and it is not surprising that collisions between such vessels was commonplace, frequently resulting in the loss of either or both vessels.

"WORRALL"

LENGTH of KEEL and FORERAKE_____ 162 FEET

BREADTH of BEAM _____ 25 "

DEPTH of HOLD _____ 17 "

SCALE ⅛" = 1 FOOT

(Nº 18).

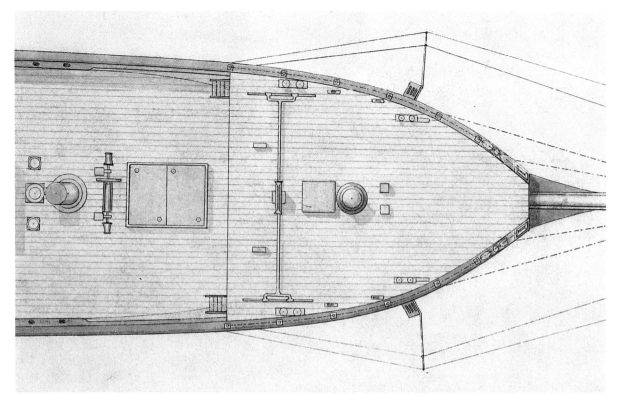

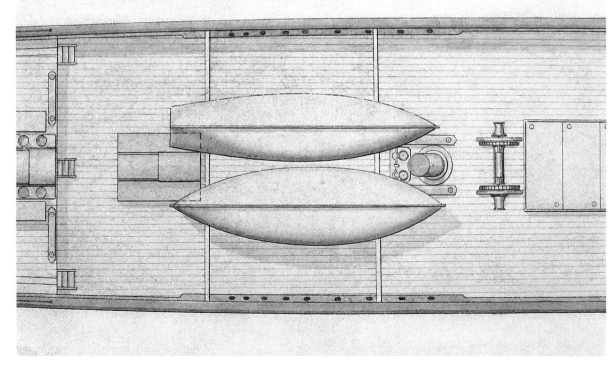

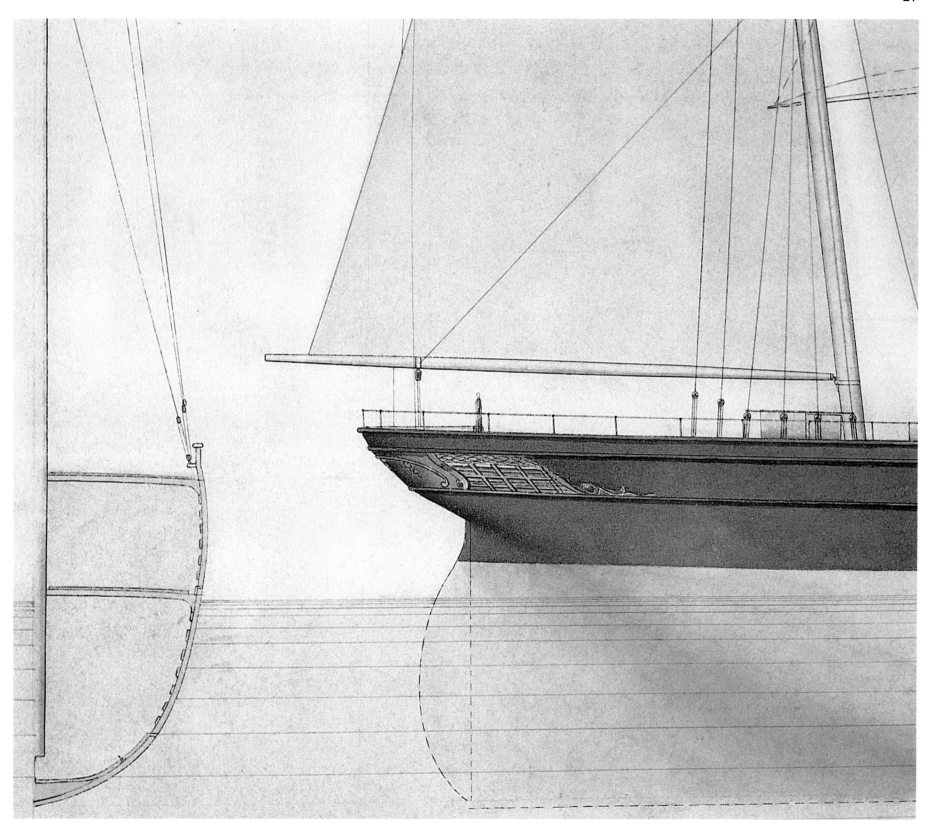

Olano

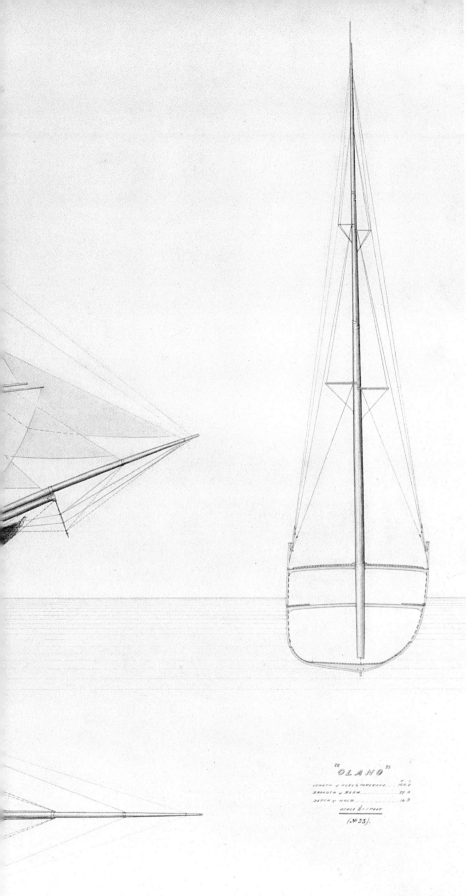

Launched 29 September 1863	**Owner** The Larrinaga Steamship
Delivered 29 September 1863	Co, Liverpool
Yard Number 23	**Gross Tonnage** 445

The completion of the *Olano* represented something of an oddity for several reasons, and also a departure from the traditional design of sailing vessels. In the first instance, the vessel was a pure sailing ship which represented a somewhat incongruous choice of propulsion for a steamship company. Secondly, it incorporated a double bottom in its construction – a feature only prevalent or necessary in steam or motor ships. Thirdly, the design was a return to the traditional hull form of a beam in direct proportion to the length, marking a departure for Harland & Wolff from the highly successful 'Belfast bottom'.

None the less, the *Olano* was a graceful and well balanced vessel which, while incorporating these rather differing standards of naval architecture, managed to operate in a highly efficient manner. The outboard profile was of a three-masted full-rigged sailing vessel. Crew accommodation was typically located at the after end. However, borrowing from the current trend in steamships, the officers' accommodation was situated between the forward and main masts; this position would have been the equivalent of forward of the funnel. In keeping with the traditional design of sailing ships though, the steering position was located at the extreme aft end, directly above the rudder.

This rather unusual little ship, which appeared to attempt to combine the best of both worlds, had a rather uneventful career – the only incident of note being a collision with the harbour wall at Heysham in October 1872, which unfortunately resulted in more damage to the *Olano* than that sustained by the harbour wall. Accidents of this nature were not surprising given the location of the steering position. However, repairs – a new bowsprit and several feet of new plates around the bow – soon saw *Olano* back in service.

Finally, this little vessel had one more and rather unique claim to fame – she was the first and only vessel launched and delivered by Harland & Wolff on the same day.

"OLANO"

LENGTH of KEEL & FORERAKE ____ 140.0
BREADTH of BEAM ____ 27.0
DEPTH of HOLD ____ 16.9

SCALE ⅛ = 1 FOOT

(N⁰ 23).

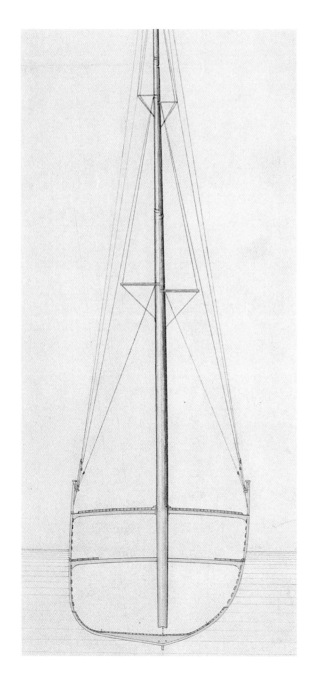

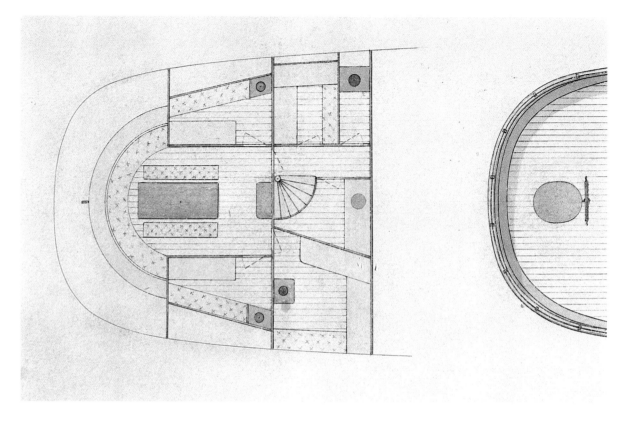

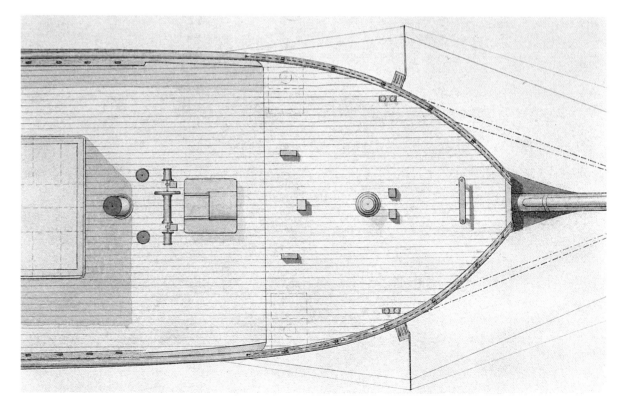

Olano

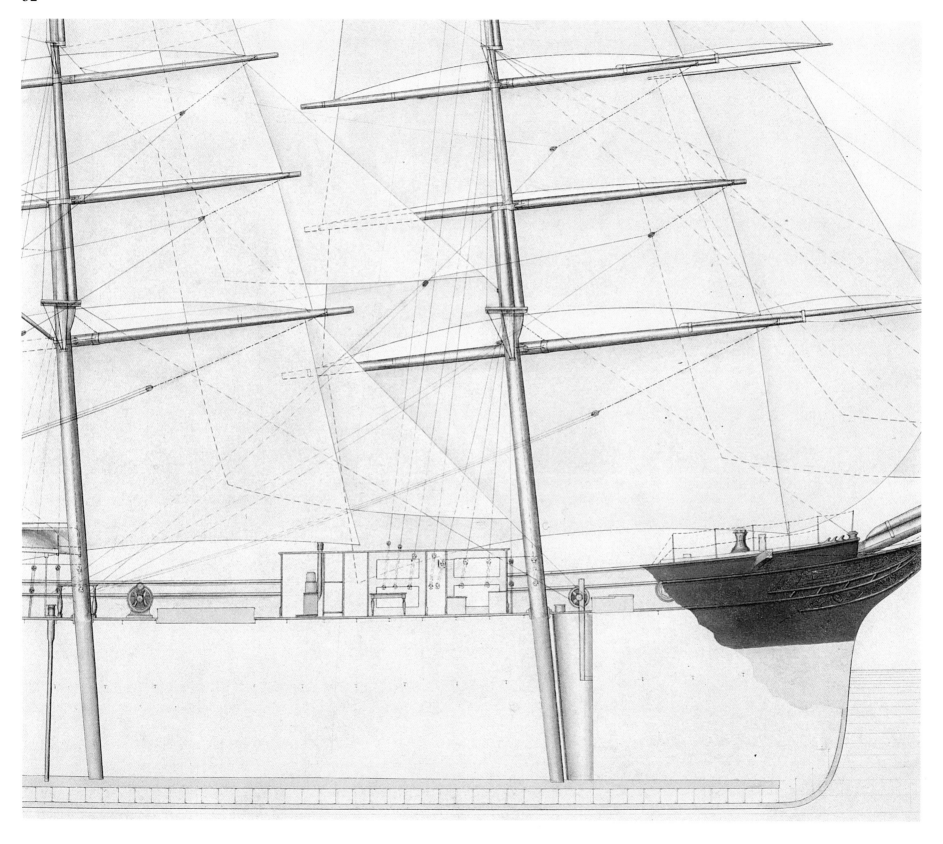

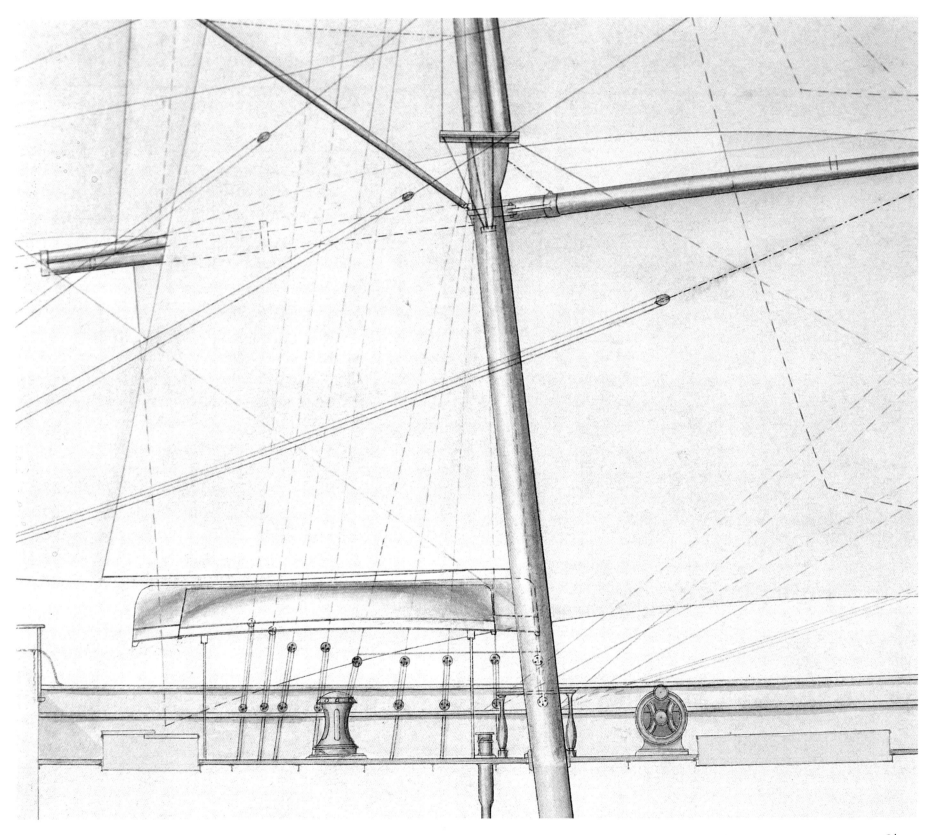

Olano

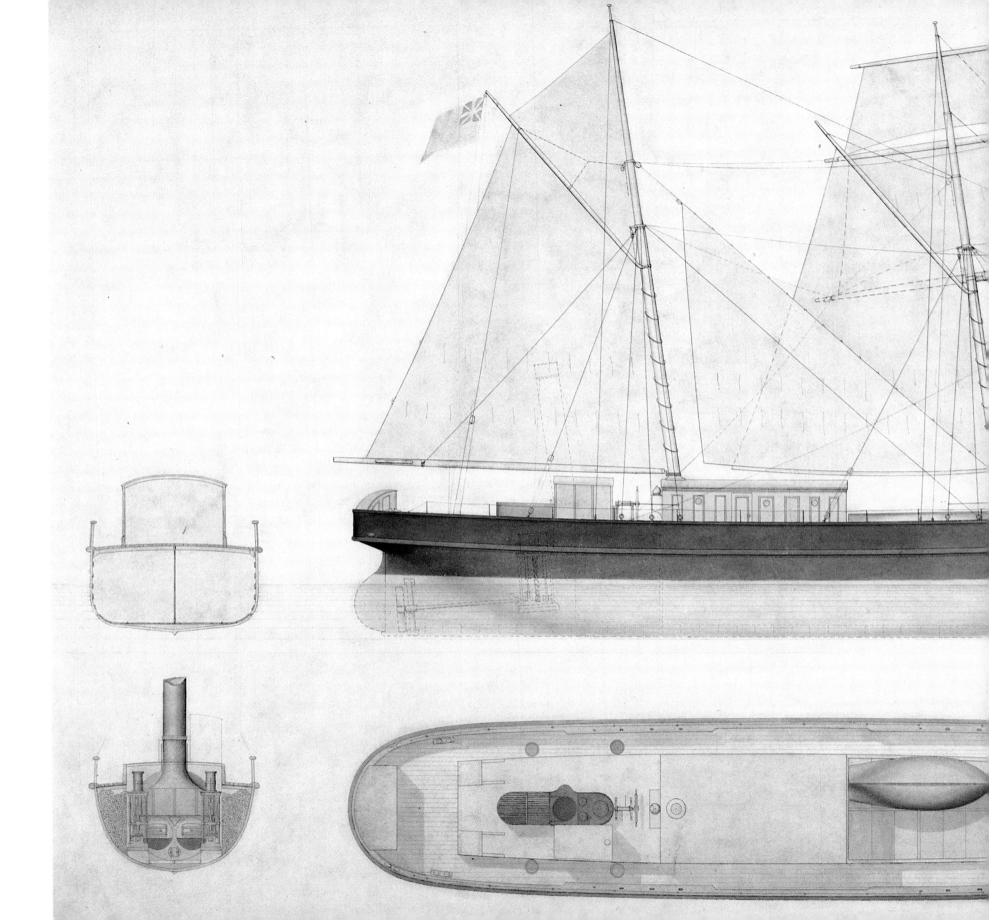

Waipara

Launched 30 October 1863	**Owner** Mr J Ritchie, Belfast
Delivered 28 November 1863	**Gross Tonnage** 90
Yard Number 26	

The coastal steamer *Waipara* was built to the specification and private use of the prominent Belfast linen merchant, Mr James Ritchie. The vessel was principally designed to ensure the safe carriage of the fine linen produced by Ritchie's flax spinning business. Irish linen was, and still is, regarded as the finest available anywhere in the world and, as such, this valuable cargo required the most careful transportation and protection against theft.

The *Waipara* was, therefore, designed with a large and uninterrupted cargo hold to facilitate the storage of large bales of linen. The hatchcovers were of considerable size, occupying almost one third of the deck forward of the crew accommodation, and were of sufficient strength to support the stowage of the ship's lifeboat. The crew accommodation comprised a raised deckhouse containing the sleeping and messing (cooking) facilities. The location of this deckhouse also had the additional advantage of overlooking the hatch, therefore making it impossible to gain access to the cargo hold without attracting the attention of the watchkeeper.

The requirement for the large cargo hold necessitated the rather unusual step of locating the engine almost at the stern of the vessel. This arrangement provided some difficulty with the arrangement of the propeller shaft, which, because of the shortness of its length, had to be directly coupled to the engine. This in turn required the engine to tilt towards the stern by some five degrees in order to ensure that the propeller shaft would have a true path of rotation. The arrangement may be studied in closer detail with reference to the drawing on page 36.

Placing a vessel's engine at the after end of the hull is a commonplace feature in ship construction today, and is almost universal in large vessels such as oil tankers and bulk carriers: however, to do so in 1863 was nothing short of revolutionary.

Waipara

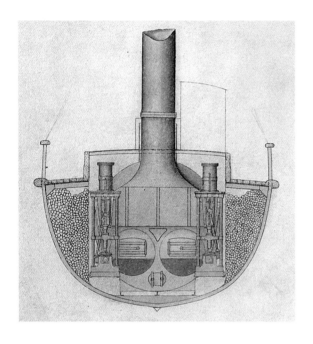

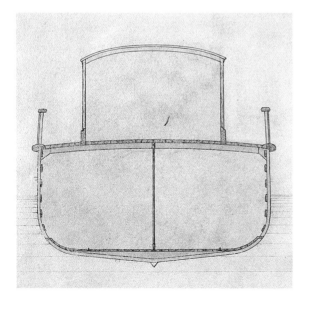

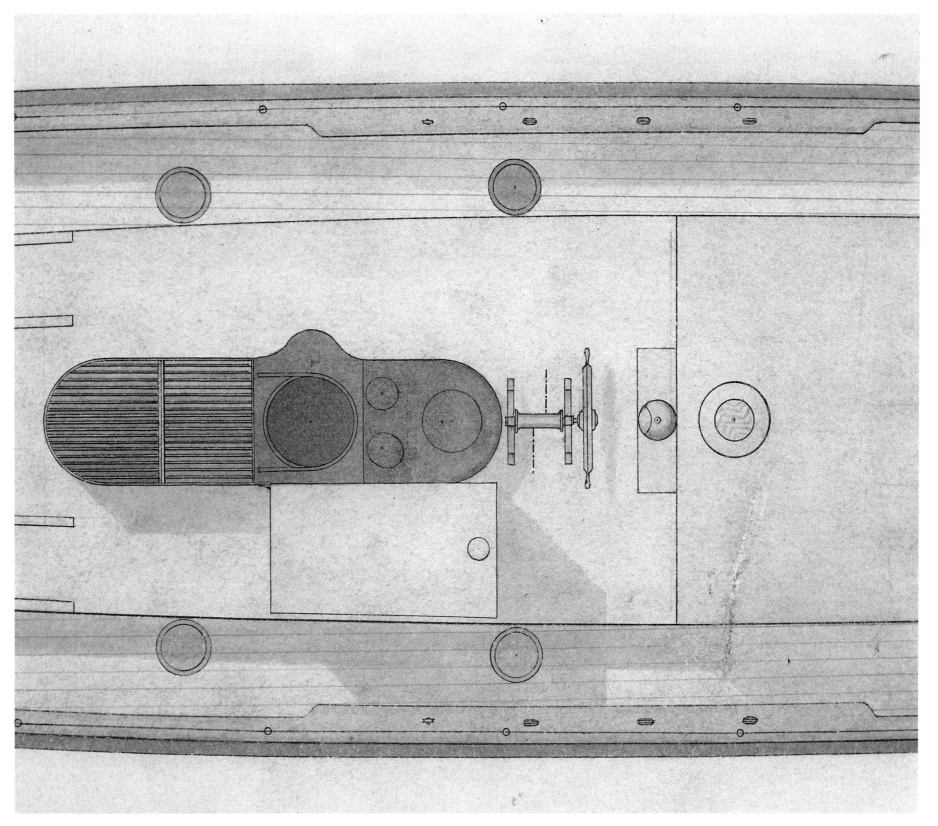

Waipara

"BARODA"

Baroda

Launched 23 April 1864	**Owner** T & J Brocklebank,
Delivered 30 April 1864	Liverpool
Yard Number 27	**Gross Tonnage** 1,364

The stunning *Baroda*, completed in 1864 for the famous Brocklebank shipping family, set new standards in both ship design and crew accommodation. The name of Brocklebank had always been associated with vessels of grace and beauty, and *Baroda* was to be no exception – with gently raked masts bedecked with top sails, gallants, and magnificent fore and main sails, which billowed far above the main deck. The bowsprit boasted no fewer than three foresails which created the impression of power and majesty; this was echoed by the fine hull form producing an elegant yet purposeful vessel.

Designed for the Brocklebank around-the-world service, the vessel had the largest possible cargo holds served through one large hatch amidships. This hatch provided access to a 'tween deck which ran the full length of the vessel and which, in turn, was provided with three internal hatches. The main or largest of these was directly below the main deck hatch with two small ones at the fore and after end.

The crew accommodation was provided in three deckhouses located at the forward, midship and after ends. The forward deckhouse housed the cook's store, galley and sail room as well as a two-berth cabin for the cook and ship's mate. Located midships was a small deckhouse providing accommodation for ten boys or apprentice seamen while at the after end stood a magnificent deckhouse which provided the accommodation for the captain and officers. Situated behind the officers' cabins was a saloon. This ran the full width of the deckhouse, affording the officers a room for their meals and a place to relax from the rigours of shipboard life. Also located here, on the port side, were two private staterooms for the use of either T or J Brocklebank, though in reality they were normally unoccupied. The general seamen were housed under this after deckhouse at the extreme stern of the vessel.

The *Baroda* remained in the Brocklebank fleet until she was scrapped in 1881.

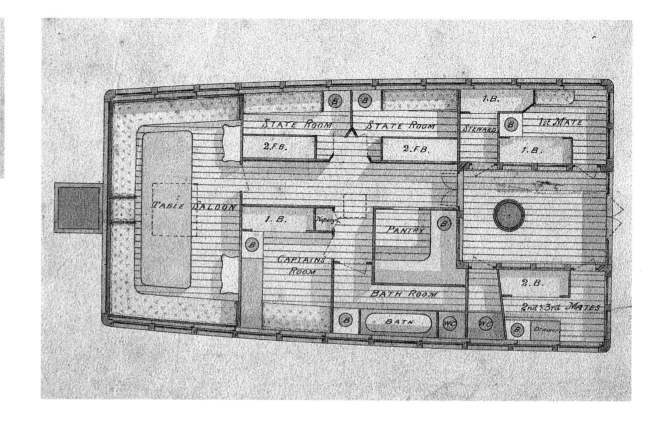

"**BARODA**"

	Feet	In
LENGTH OF KEEL AND FORERAKE	225	0
BREADTH OF BEAM	36	6
DEPTH OF HOLD (top of Floors)	23	11
REGISTER TONNAGE	1364 Tons	

SCALE ⅛ INCH = 1 FOOT.

(Nº 27).

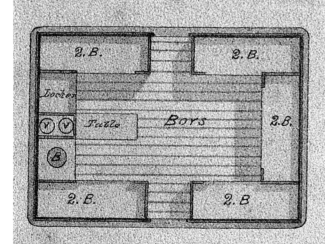

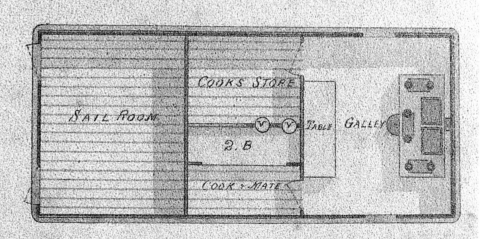

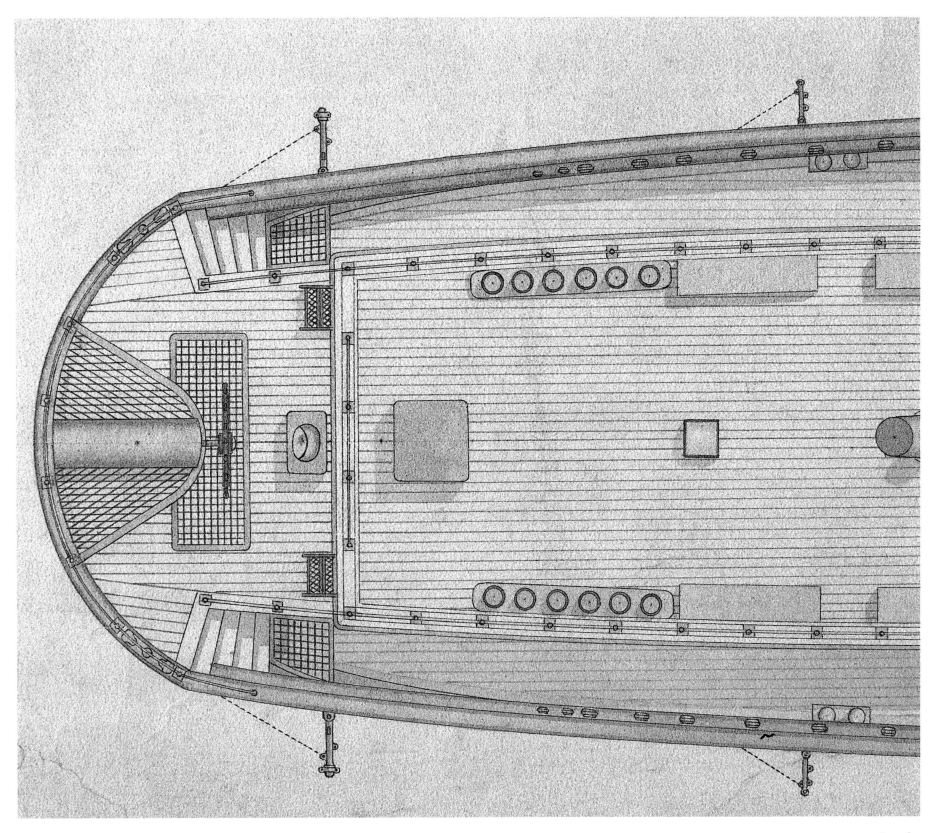

Baroda

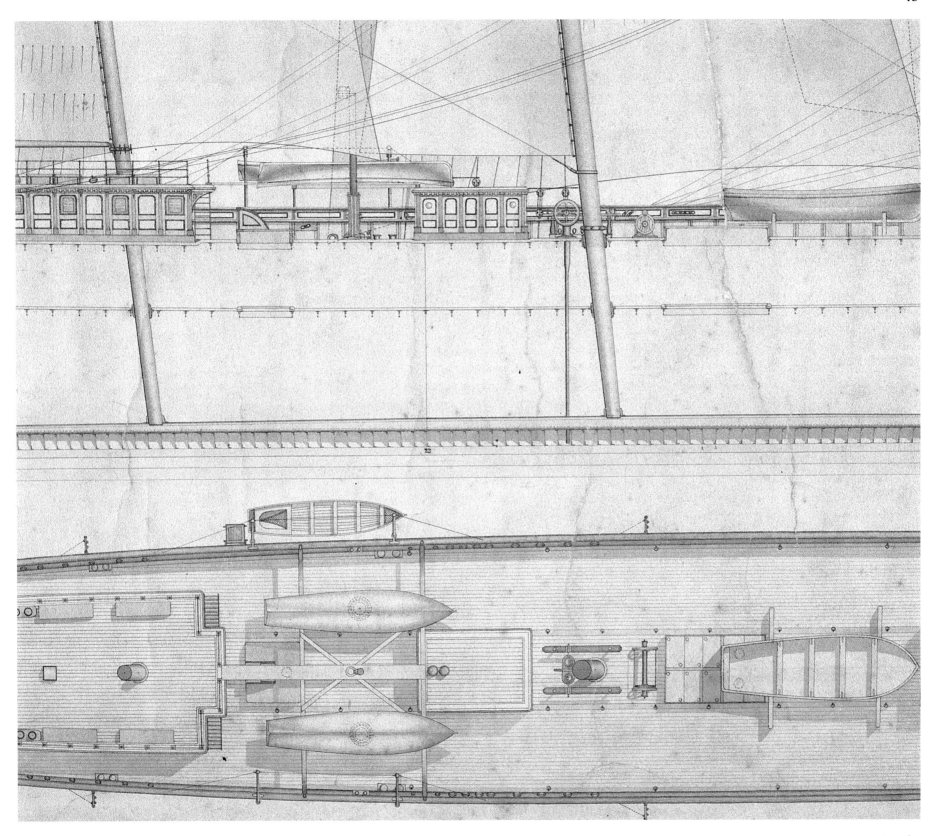

Baroda

Dharwar

DHARWAR.

Launched 3 September 1864	**Owner** The Iron Ship Company
Delivered 27 September 1864	Limited, Belfast
Yard Number 30	**Gross Tonnage** 1,456

The *Dharwar*, built for the unimaginatively named Iron Ship Company Limited, was a graceful and appealing vessel. Designed for the burgeoning trade routes to India, the vessel received an Indian name which was reputed to mean virtue. Regrettably, the same quality could not be applied to the owners. A one-ship operation, the Iron Ship Company Limited soon fell into financial difficulties. In 1871 these forced the sale of its only vessel to C T Bowring & Company, who would sell her to the British and Indian Shipping Company two years later.

Despite this inauspicious beginning, the *Dharwar* proved a reliable and popular ship, trading from the United Kingdom to the jewel in the crown of the British Empire, India. The design was based on the successful 'Belfast bottom', although the forward end had an unusually broad beam which give rise to a pronounced taper at the stern. Principally engaged in the carriage of general household goods from the United Kingdom, and usually returning with spices and tea from India, the *Dharwar* also provided accommodation in twin berth state-rooms for sixteen passengers, usually high ranking civil servants or army officers, accompanied by their wives, embarking on a long period of duty. A steward was provided to serve their meals in the large saloon located in the centre of their accommodation. This saloon became the focal point of shipboard life and would have been the scene of many enjoyable evenings as the passengers whiled away the long voyage to India.

Things, however, were not so pleasant or comfortable for the crew, most of whom were located below the main deck at the forward end where they experienced the full motion of the ship as it traversed the seas. This accommodation was stiflingly hot in the Indian climate, especially in summer, yet freezing cold in the British winter. No method of heating or ventilation was permitted below decks and the crew would often take to sleeping on deck when in the tropics. This would inevitably mean being bitten by mosquitoes which frequently resulted in malaria.

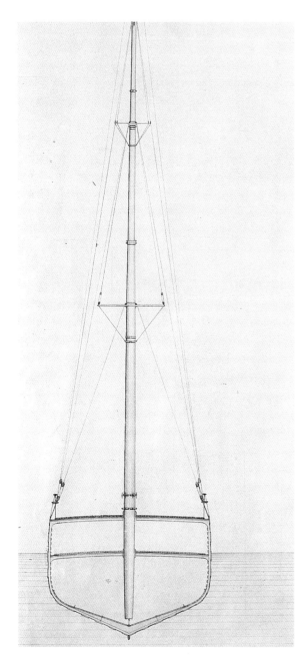

"DHARWAR."

	Feet.	Ins.
LENGTH OF KEEL AND FORERAKE	220	0
BREADTH OF BEAM	37	0
DEPTH OF HOLD (TOP OF FLOORS)	24	0
REGISTER TONNAGE	1293·06	

SCALE ⅛ INCH = 1 FOOT.

(Nº 30)

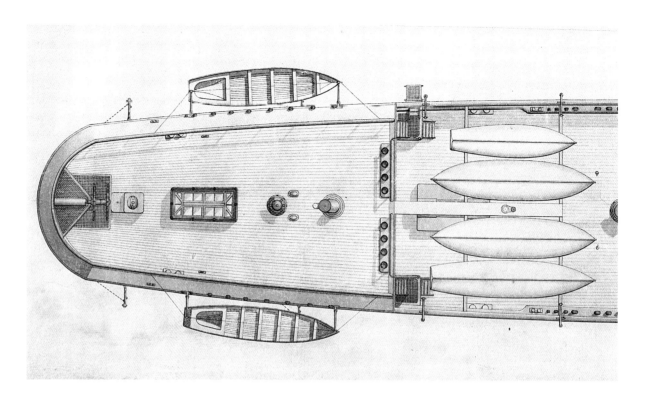

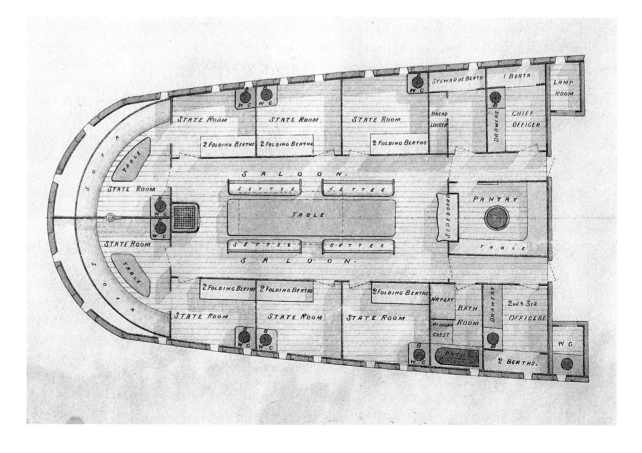

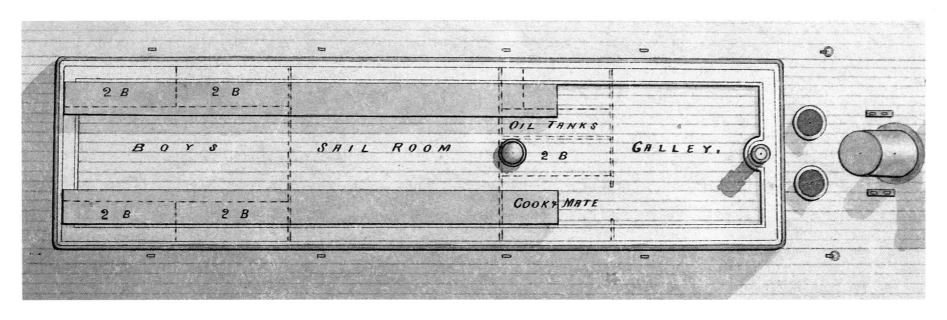

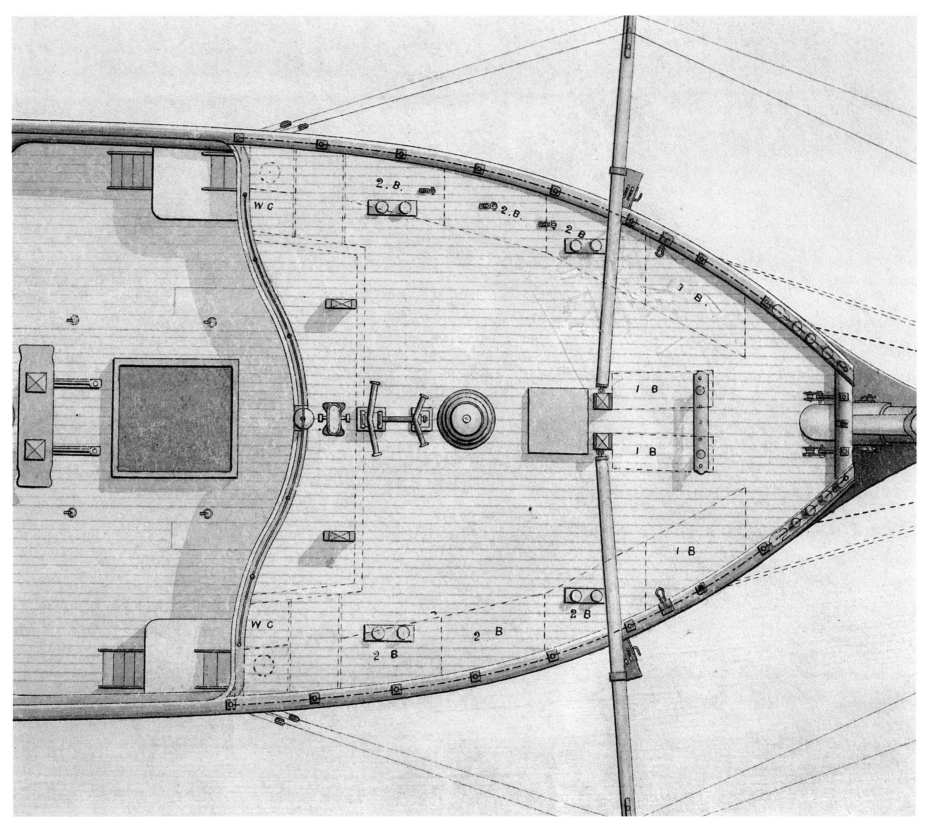

Dharwar

Douro

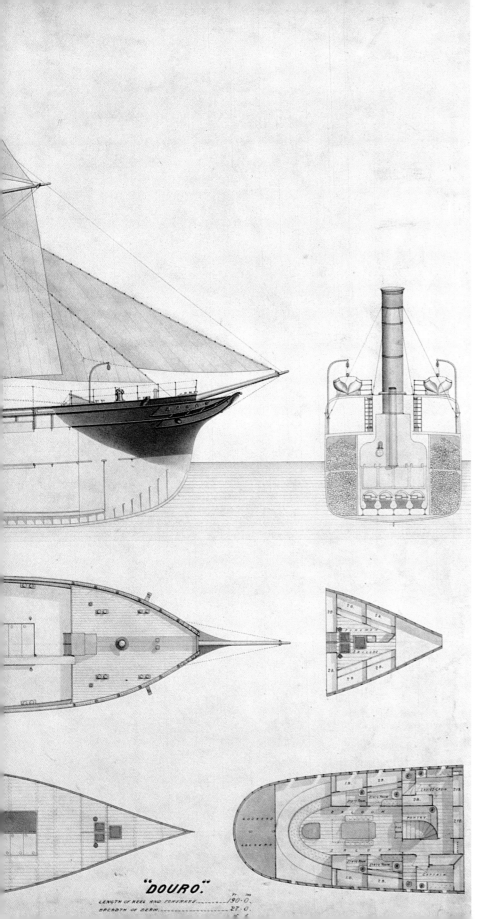

"DOURO."
LENGTH OF KEEL AND FORERAKE..........190·0·
BREADTH OF BEAM..........27·0·

Launched 2 November 1864	Owner John Bibby Sons & Co,
Delivered 24 November 1864	Liverpool
Yard Number 31	Gross Tonnage 528

The completion of the *Douro* marked the twelfth vessel constructed by Harland & Wolff for the Bibby company since 1859 – a remarkable achievement in just six years. This association would continue right up to the present day, but would never see the like again of the remarkable *Douro*.

Specifically designed for Bibby's South African service, in fact the *Douro* saw service in all parts of the globe, circumnavigating the world on at least fifteen occasions. Completed as a 'tween deck general cargo vessel, *Douro* was equipped with the very latest cargo handling equipment and the most modern design of steam engine. The vessel had three main hatch covers located on the main deck and servicing three complementary hatches directly below on the 'tween or intermediate deck. This arrangement ensured that various cargoes could be kept separate from each other and loaded in order, according to ports of discharge. That is to say that cargo for the first port of call would be loaded last so that it would be immediately available for discharge on arrival.

The 'tween deck itself was constructed of timber spars as were the sides of the cargo hold, a method of construction which provided considerable insulating properties when carrying a perishable cargo. With the advances in marine engineering the reliability of the early steam engines had been much improved and this led to a further reduction in the number of sails considered necessary. Progressive shipowners such as the Bibbys still did not place all their trust in steam, that would come later; for the present they were content to have a 'belt and braces' arrangement and thus enjoy the benefit of both worlds.

On the whole, the crew were still accommodated under the main deck at the forward end, with the master and officers midships; however, with *Douro*, Harland & Wolff introduced a novel accommodation arrangement at the stern. For the first time a tiered arrangement was employed, comprising two levels under the main deck in which could be found the passenger staterooms for eight people in twin berths, together with a special ladies' cabin directly adjacent to the captain's. On the deck above was a private promenade on which the passengers could take the air and enjoy the voyage in comfort away from the oppressive heat of the cabins below. Unfortunately it would still be some years before the advent of air conditioning made life on board a vessel in the tropics comfortable.

Some records say that the *Douro* was wrecked off the Cape of Good Hope, South Africa in 1879, reputedly while carrying a cargo of gold bullion, although a wreck has not been found to verify this. The official Bibby Line history shows her to have been sold to the Leyland Line, under whose ownership she was renamed *Alceria* and, later, *Camilla*, *Cephalonia*, and *Nilos*. She was broken up in 1927.

Douro

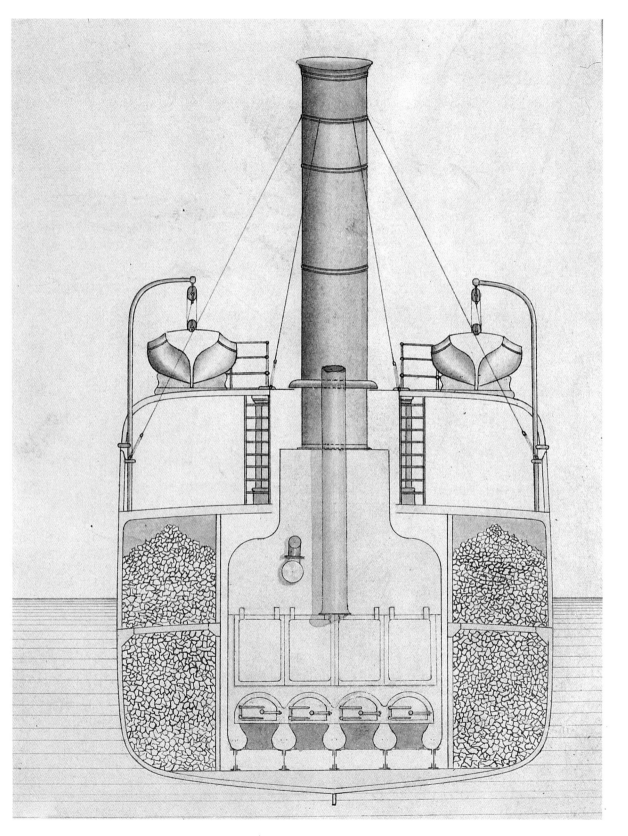

"DOURO."

	Ft	Ins
LENGTH OF KEEL AND FORERAKE	190	0
BREADTH OF BEAM	27	0
DEPTH OF HOLD	15	6
REGISTER TONNAGE	528	52

SCALE ⅛ = 1 FOOT.

(No 31)

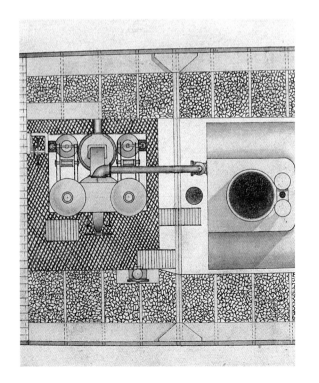

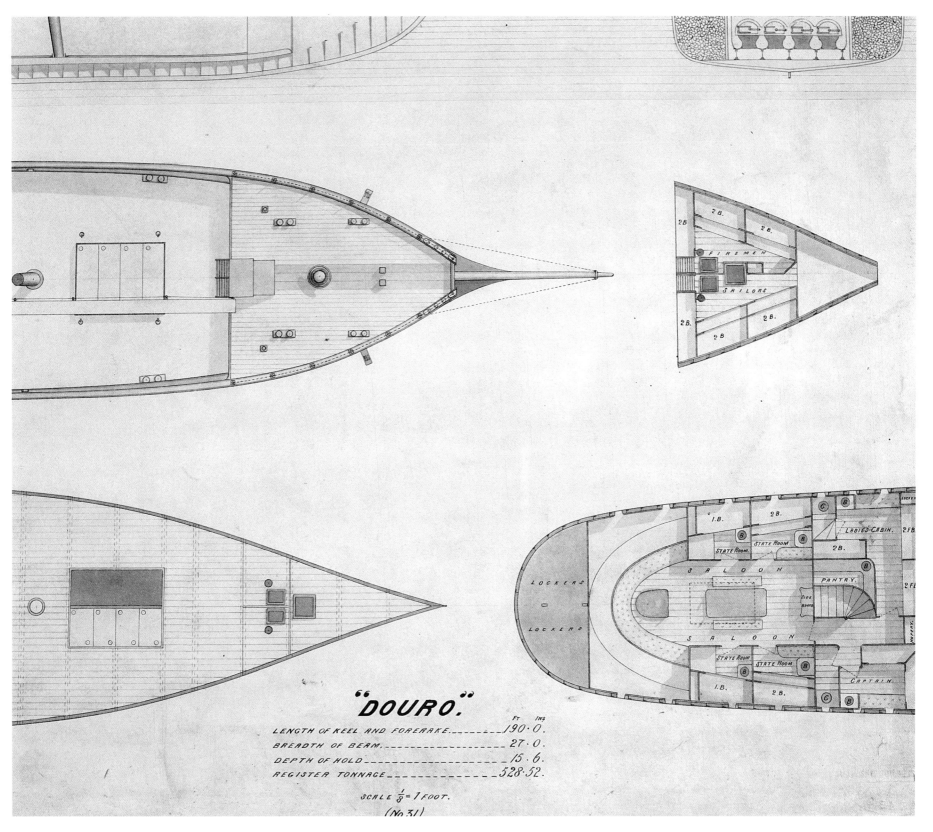

"DOURO."

	Ft	Ins
LENGTH OF KEEL AND FORERAKE	190	0
BREADTH OF BEAM	27	0
DEPTH OF HOLD	15	6
REGISTER TONNAGE	528	52

SCALE ⅛ = 1 FOOT.

(No 31)

Douro

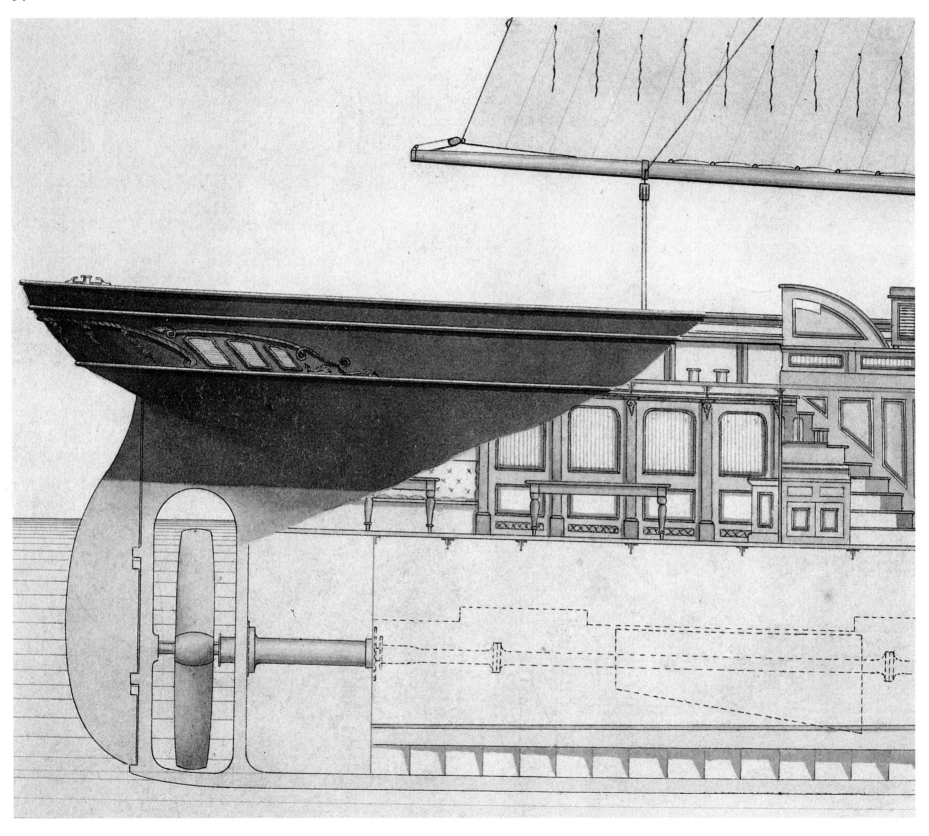

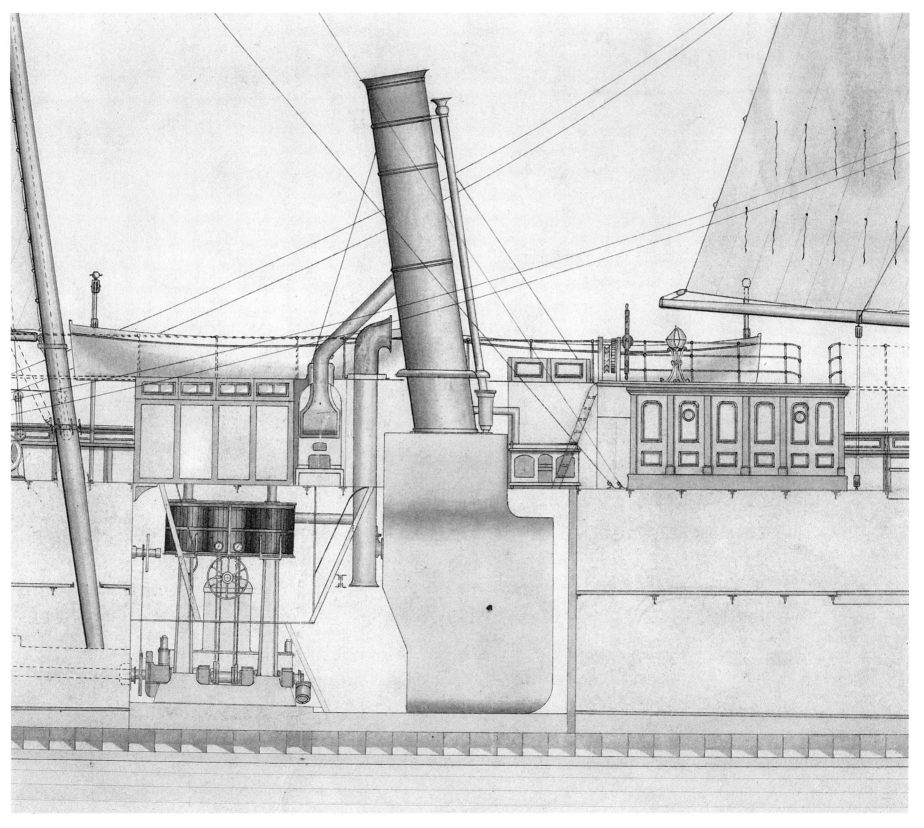

Douro

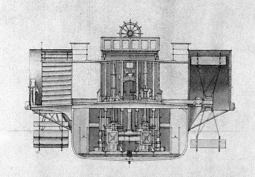

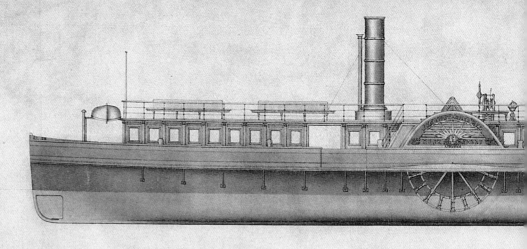

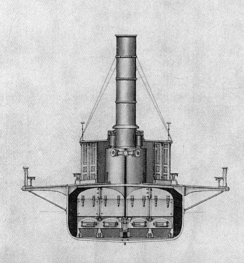

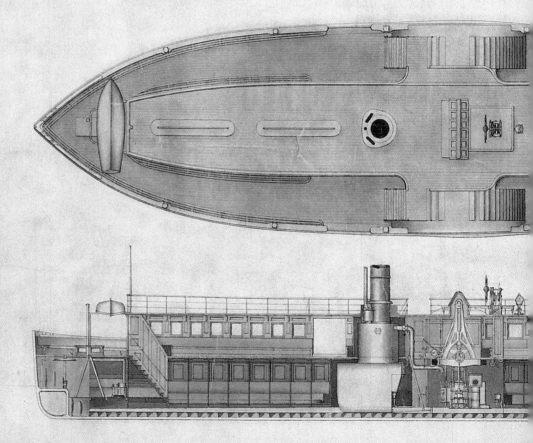

N<u>os</u> 38. & 39.

GYPSY QUEEN. & FAIRY QUEEN.

LENGTH 135. F. 10. BREADTH 20. F.
DEPTH from TOP of CEILING, 8 FT. 11.
CYLINDERS, 35. DIAMS. STROKE, 42.
NOMINAL HORSE POWER, 70.
REGISTER TONNAGE, 148.89.
GROSS TONNAGE, 148.89.
BUILDERS TONNAGE, 263 $\frac{31}{94}$

SCALE $\frac{1}{8}$ IN = FOOT.

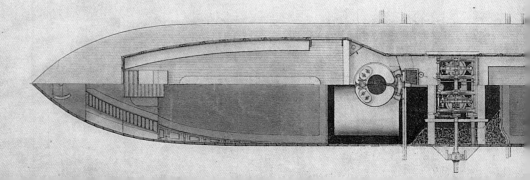

Gypsy Queen
& Fairy Queen

	Gypsy Queen	Fairy Queen
Launched	11 July 1865	11 July 1865
Delivered	24 July 1865	24 July 1865
Yard Number	38	39
Owner	The Rock Ferry Company, Gibraltar	
GrossTonnage	149	149

Twin sisters in every respect, the *Gypsy Queen* and *Fairy Queen* were built in tandem on the same slipway, being launched with only a fifteen-minute interval between them. This somewhat unusual arrangement was not without difficulty as, during the launch of the first vessel, it soon became evident that the second vessel was becoming difficult to retain on its launch bed due to the vibration.

Built for the short crossing between Gibraltar and Tangier, these little ferries required a tremendously powerful engine to combat the strong current found at the mouth of the Mediterranean. The solution was found in an adaptation of the steam engine designed by George Stephenson to power his *Rocket* locomotive. The propulsive force comprised of a twin-cylinder single-acting steam engine, each cylinder having a diameter of thirty-five inches with a stroke or piston travel of forty-two inches. This simple arrangement provided a power output of some seventy horsepower directly driving twin paddle wheels at each side of the vessel. Each of the paddle wheels had a 'feathering' arrangement enabling the blades on each wheel to be finely adjusted to reduce vibration and shock as each blade entered the water. Passengers were accommodated for the short journey in a large deckhouse, where seating was limited to four small benches along the centre line of the vessel. However, a wide expanse of open deck was available for those who preferred to remain in the open.

A unique feature of these ferries was the arrangement of a bow at each end, each being fitted with a rudder for steering purposes. This arrangement alleviated the need for the vessel to turn around before departure and thus provided a faster service than conventional ferries.

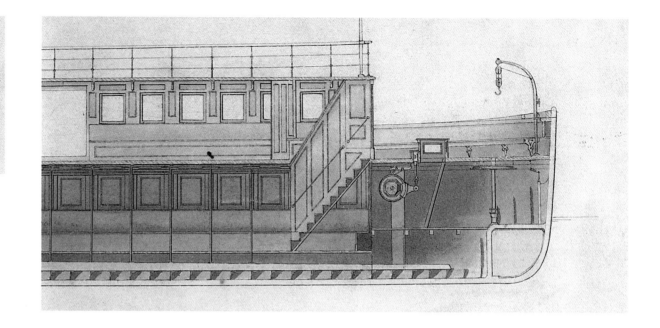

Nº<u>s</u> 38. & 39.

GYPSY QUEEN. & FAIRY QUEEN.

LENGTH 135.F<u>T</u> 10. BREADTH 20,F<u>T</u>.
DEPTH from TOP of CEILING, 8 FT. 11.
CYLINDERS, 35, DIAM<u>S</u> STROKE, 42.
NOMINAL HORSE POWER, 70.
REGISTER TONNAGE, 148,89.
GROSS TONNAGE, 148,89.
BUILDERS TONNAGE, 263 $\frac{39}{94}$.

SCALE $\frac{1}{8}$<u>IN</u> = FOOT.

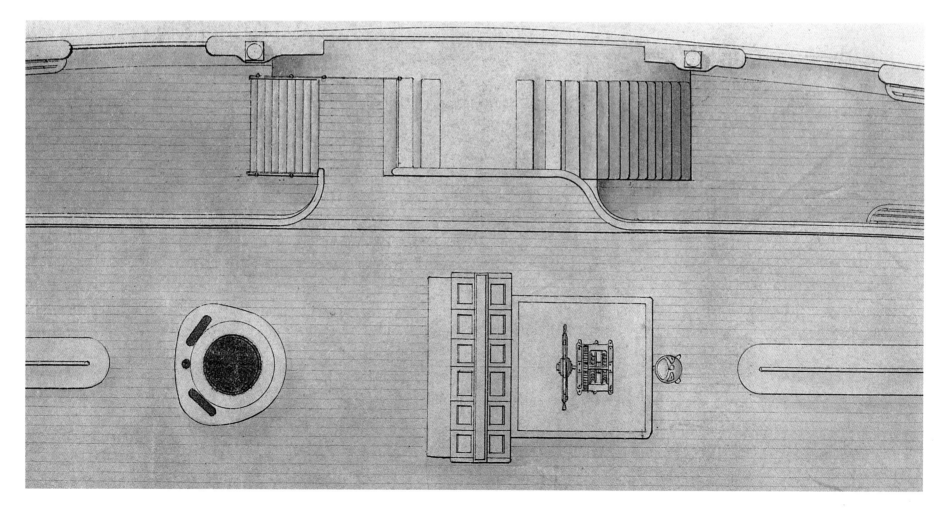

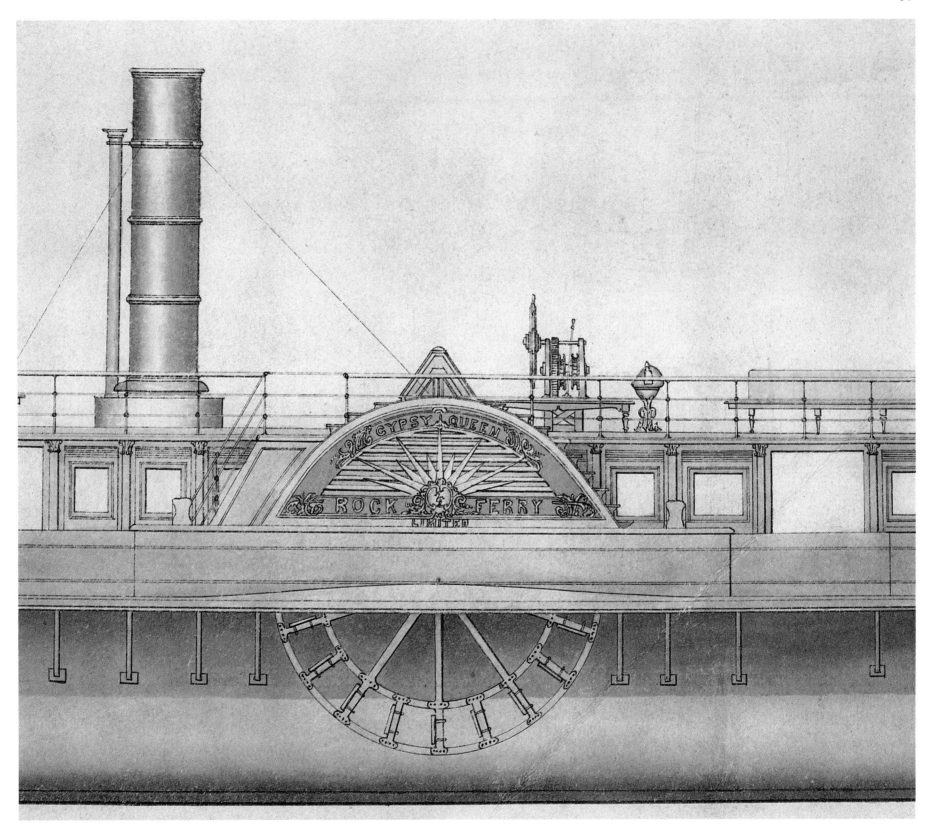

Gypsy Queen & Fairy Queen

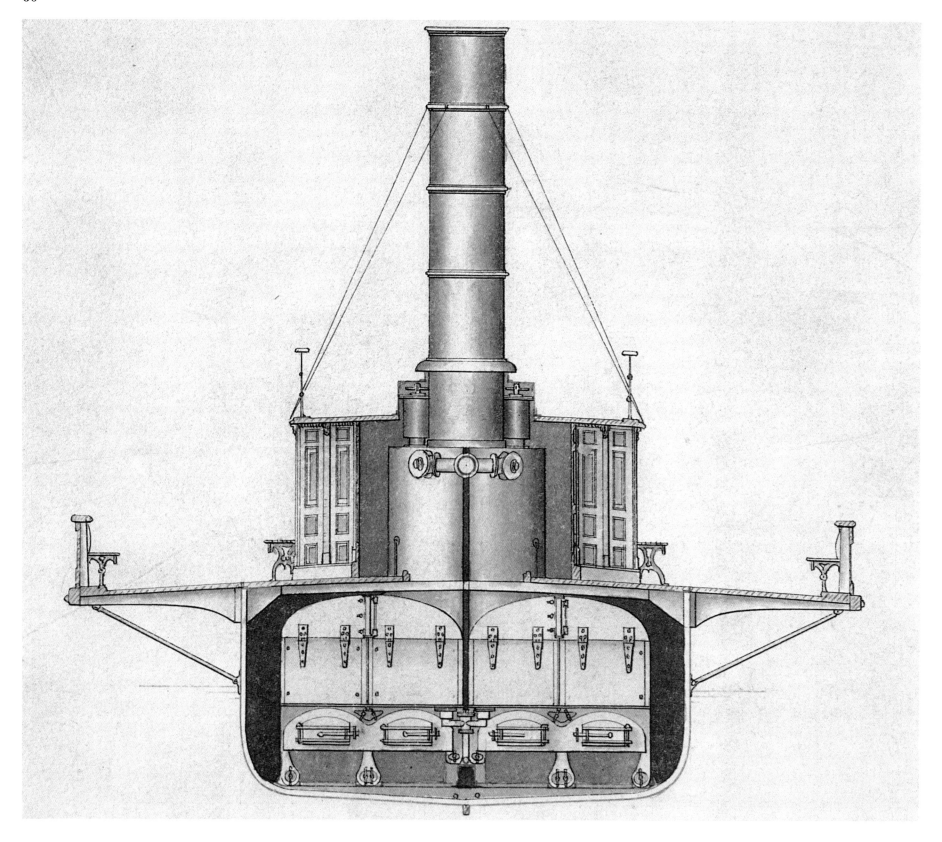

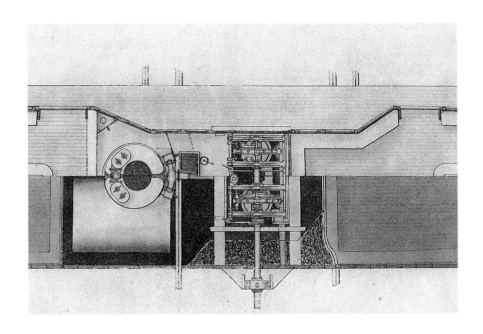

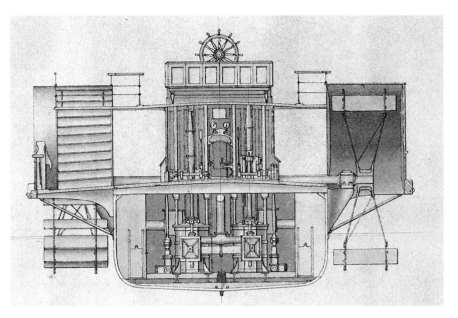

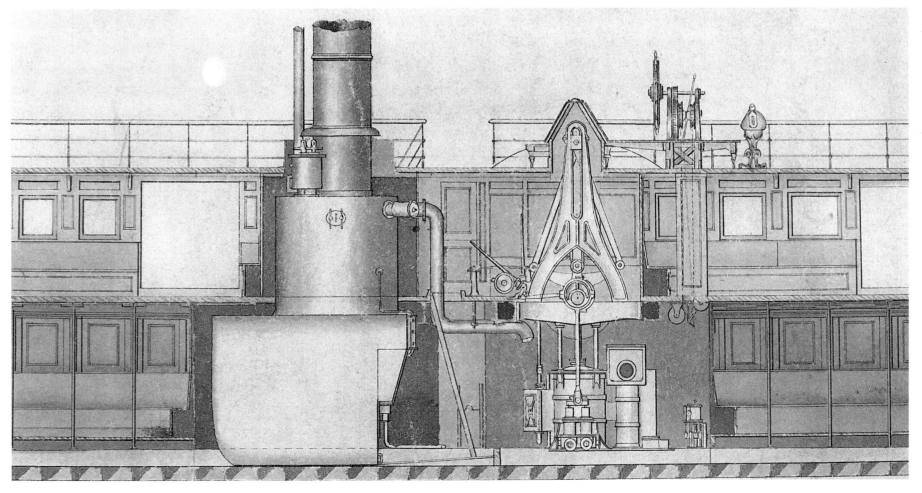

Gypsy Queen & Fairy Queen

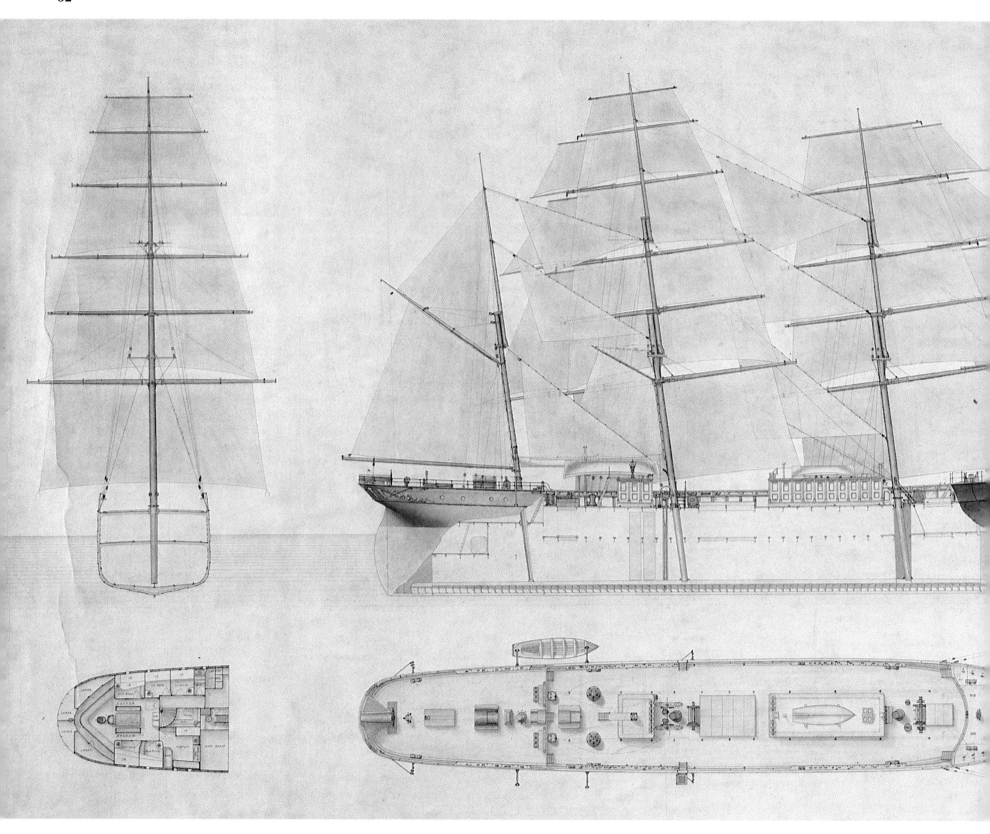

Broughton

Launched 25 January 1868	**Owner** Ismay, Imrie & Company,
Delivered 30 January 1868	Liverpool
Yard Number 44	**Gross Tonnage** 602

The history of the *Broughton* plays a very special part in the history of Harland & Wolff in that it very nearly caused the closure of the company. Harland & Wolff was completing work on its first Admiralty order, a 'Brecon' class gun boat, HMS *Lynx*; however, because of the financial constraints imposed by the Admiralty, all such contracts were on a fixed price basis. Due to a combination of factors this would result in a loss on this contract of £5,000. To complicate matters further, the original owner for the *Broughton* had been declared bankrupt, thus leaving the vessel to be completed at Harland & Wolff's expense. The consequence of these unfortunate circumstances resulted in the company being pushed firmly into the red with little prospect of recovery.

Things could not have been very much worse when into the picture stepped Gustav Schwabe, Wolff's uncle who introduced the partners to Thomas Henry Ismay. Ismay had, with Schwabe's assistance, recently purchased the bankrupt White Star Line. Ismay quickly needed to acquire new tonnage to maintain the old White Star service to Australia and the gold fields of New South Wales. The almost completed *Broughton* was ideally suited to his purpose and, provided that Schwabe would supply one quarter of the finance in the form of a loan to Harland and Wolff, the purchase was completed.

In honour of this arrangement it was agreed to name the vessel after the saviour of the hour, and accordingly the new vessel received the name *Broughton* after Broughton Hall, Gustav Schwabe's Liverpool home.

The purchase of this vessel and the introduction of Thomas Ismay to the two partners was to set in motion a train of events which would have tragic consequences, culminating in the construction of RMS *Titanic* for the White Star Line. *Broughton* only remained in the White Star fleet for eight years until she was disposed of by Thomas Ismay to William Thomas & Company of Swansea who operated her successfully for several years until disposing of her in 1899. *Broughton* sank in 1902 on a voyage from Hamburg to Glasgow.

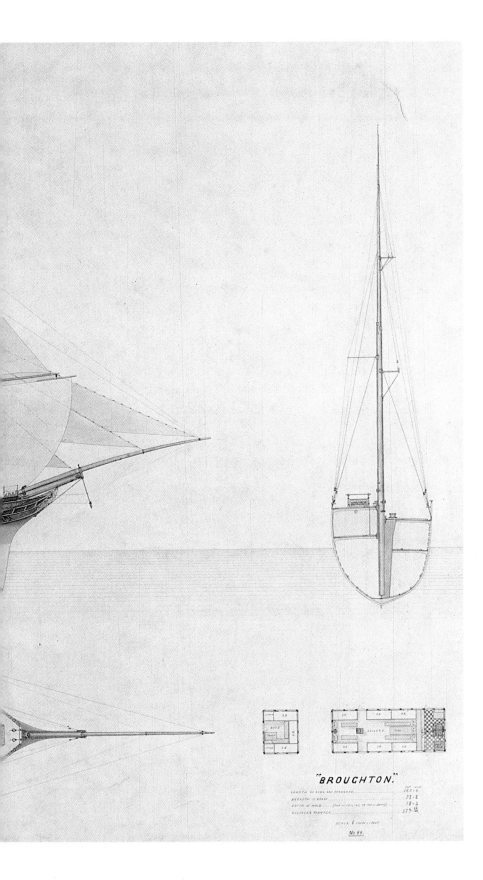

"BROUGHTON."

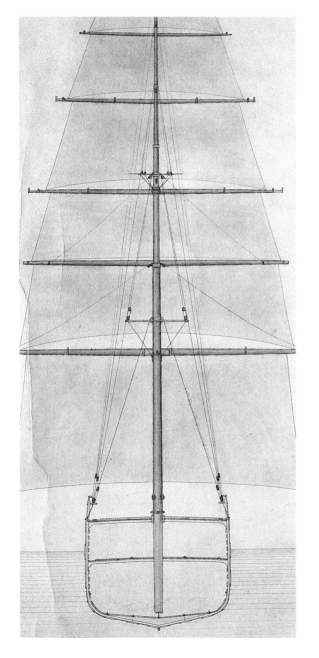

"BROUGHTON."

	FEET	INCHES
LENGTH OF KEEL AND FORERAKE	165	4.
BREADTH OF BEAM	27	8.
DEPTH OF HOLD (TOP OF CEILING TO TOP OF BEAM)	18	3.
REGISTER TONNAGE	579·$\frac{88}{100}$	

SCALE $\frac{1}{8}$ INCH = 1 FOOT

No 44.

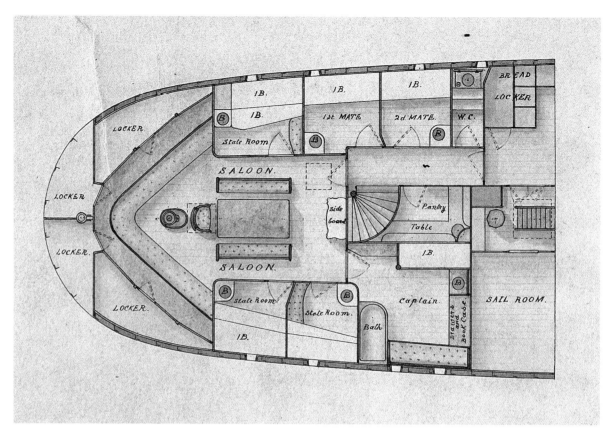

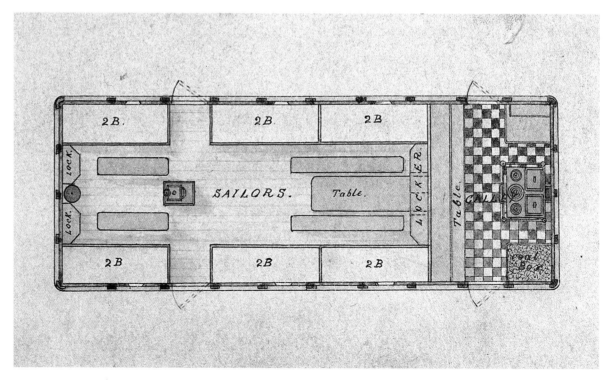

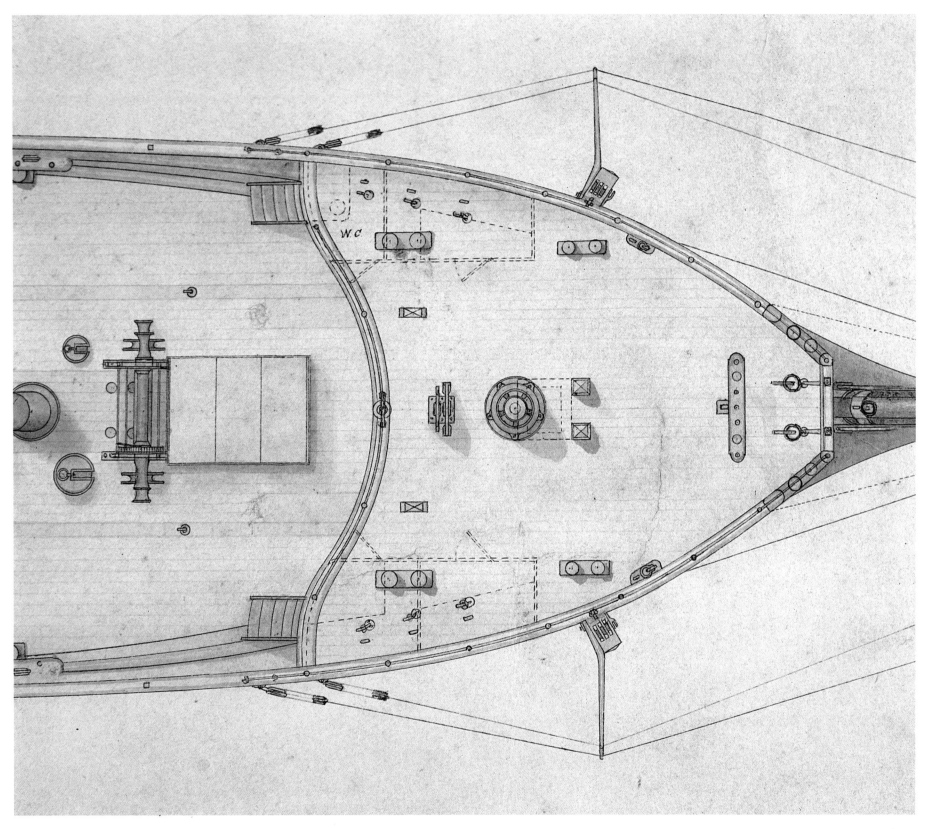

W.C

Broughton

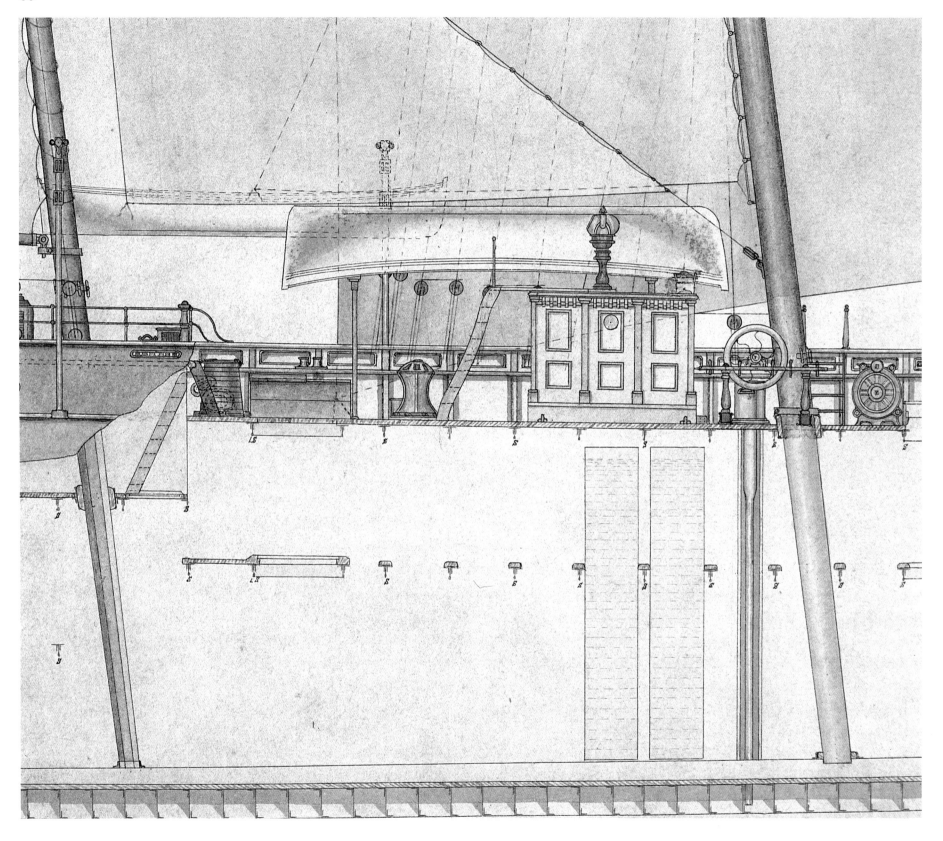

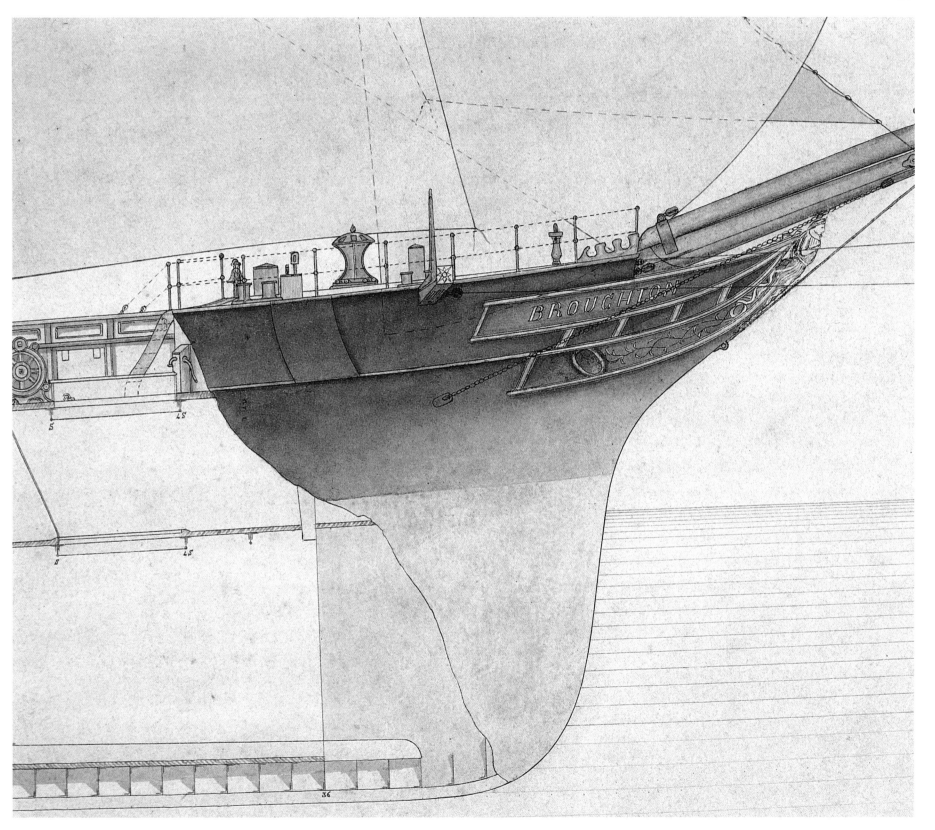

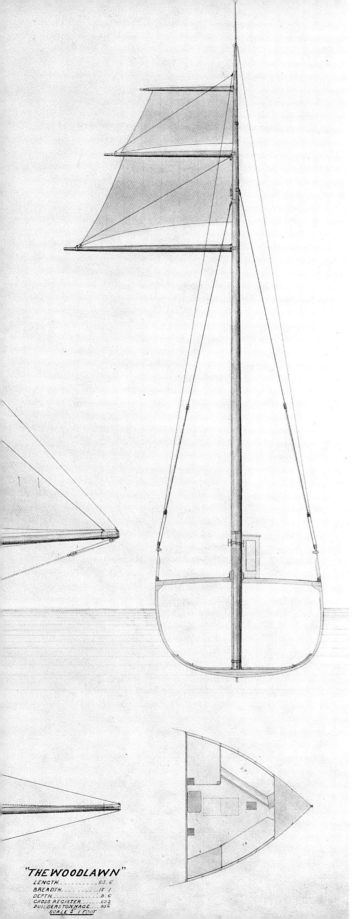

"THE WOODLAWN"
LENGTH............65.6
BREADTH............17.1
DEPTH............8.6
GROSS REGISTER............522
BUILDERS TONNAGE............63
SCALE ⅛ / 1 FOOT

The Woodlawn

Launched 24 June 1868	**Owner** Mr S Moreland, Belfast
Delivered 30 June 1868	**Gross Tonnage** 63
Yard Number 56	

Harland & Wolff were now a well established firm of shipbuilders and engineers who were being courted by the major shipping companies of the day to fulfil requirements for bigger and better vessels. The partners were reluctant to refuse an order from any source though, as demonstrated by the construction of the tiny schooner *Woodlawn* for the private ownership of Mr S Moreland. A typical schooner design, this workhorse of the sea was unremarkable in its appearance, yet for all that still displayed the charm evident in many sailing vessels. The short bowsprit with its single sail leading up to the foremast provided an air of simple, yet understated, elegance.

This tiny vessel was completed in just over four months, the keel being laid on 22 February 1868. The vessel had nothing in the way of crew accommodation and was intended only for short voyages to English and Scottish west coast ports. Typical of the small coastal trading vessels of the period, a careful study of the drawings will indicate the almost complete absence of anything other than the basic necessities for the comfort of the crew. Intended for voyages of a short duration, in reality, delays were commonplace. In spite of this the owners did not regard the comfort of the crew as a requirement.

Woodlawn had an uneventful career and ended as a rotting hulk near the town of Bangor on the County Down coast of Northern Ireland in 1875.

The Woodlawn

"THE WOODLAWN"

LENGTH	65.6
BREADTH	17.1
DEPTH	8.6
CROSS REGISTER	62.2
BUILDERS TONNAGE	85¾

SCALE ⅜" 1 FOOT

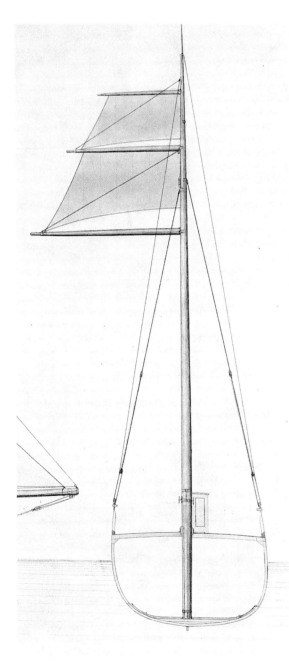

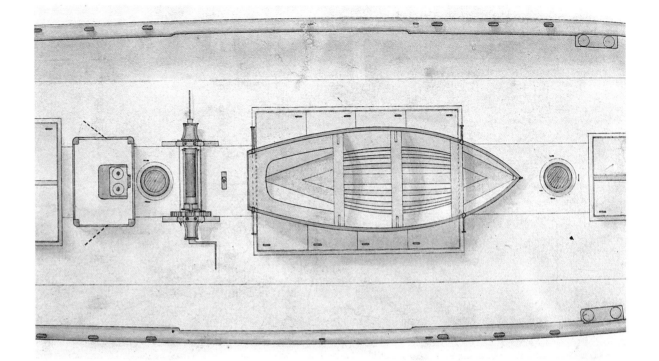

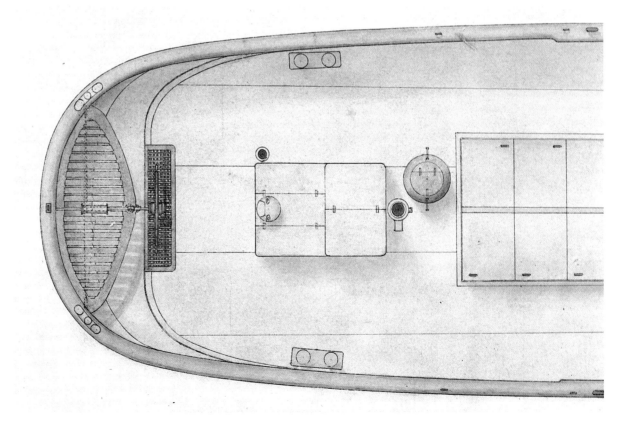

The Woodlawn

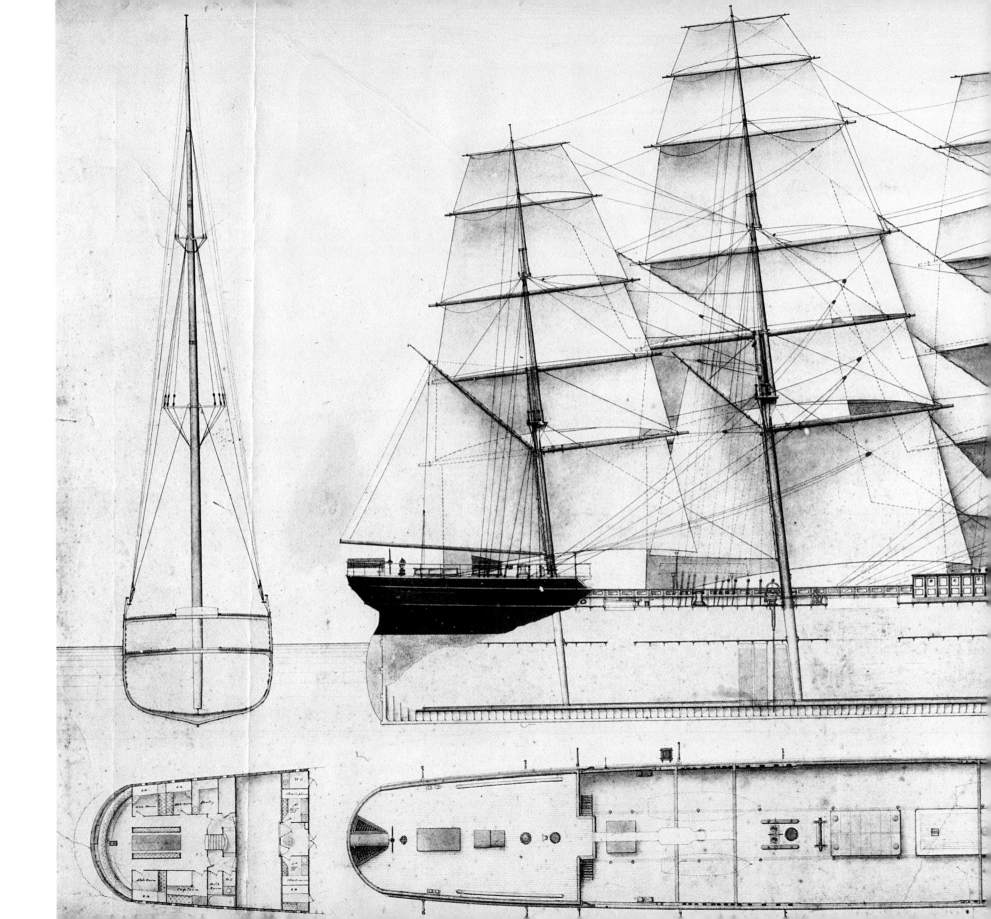

Juliet

"JULIET"

Launched 1 January 1869	**Owner** C T Bowring & Co,
Delivered 23 January 1869	London
Yard Number 58	**Gross Tonnage** 1,301

The *Juliet* was of the classic three-masted clipper ship design regarded as the greyhound of the seas. This magnificent vessel, together with others of her type, opened up the trade routes across the globe, bringing tea from India and the Far East, silks from China and the new material of cotton from the Americas.

The *Juliet* differed in some respects from the usual vessel specification in that, rather than have the Harland & Wolff patented steel and cement deck, Bowring specified that the traditional teak decking be used on the upper deck and exposed surfaces. However, not wishing to compromise the strength of the vessel, it was agreed that the teak should be laid over rather than replace the steel deck.

The vessel was of the standard 'tween deck construction with three cargo hatches: the main one was amidships with a smaller hatch located at each of the forward and after ends. Fresh water tanks were provided aft of the fore and main masts with ballast water tanks being located in the fore peak and double bottom. Crew accommodation was provided for seamen under the main deck at the forward end, with officer accommodation and mess facilities located in a deckhouse immediately behind the foremast. The captain's cabin, together with accommodation for six passengers in three twin-berth staterooms, was located under the main deck at the stern.

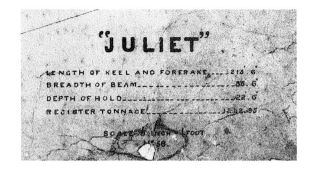

"JULIET"

LENGTH OF KEEL AND FORERAKE .... 213.6'
BREADTH OF BEAM .... 35.6'
DEPTH OF HOLD .... 22.6'
REGISTER TONNAGE 1252.95

SCALE 3 INCH 1 FOOT
N° 58

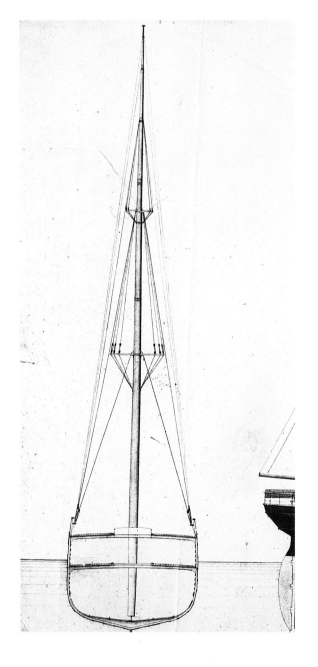

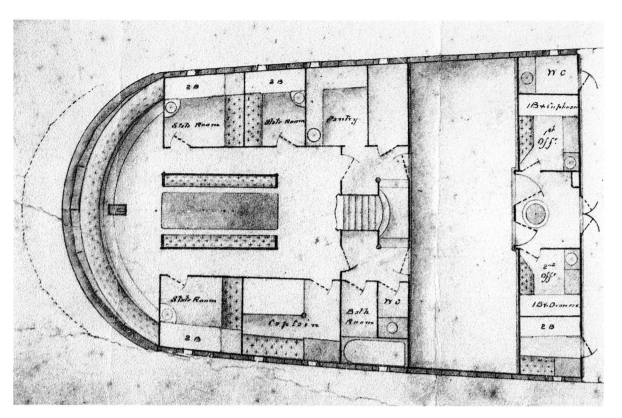

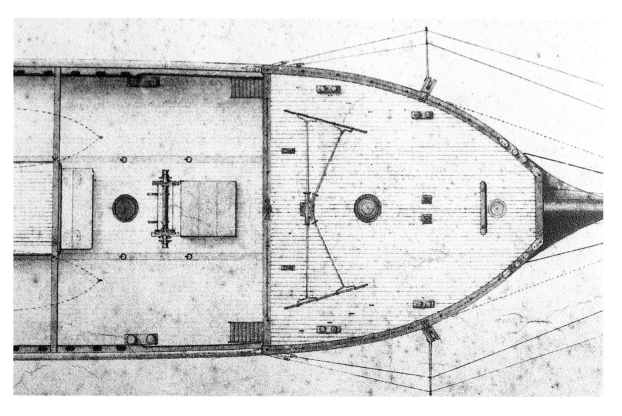

Juliet

Bavarian, Bulgarian & Bohemian

	Bavarian	*Bulgarian*	*Bohemian*
Launched	7 October 1869	17 February 1870	16 April 1870
Delivered	5 November 1869	20 March 1870	29 May 1870
Yard Number	68	70	71
Owners	John Bibby Sons & Co, Liverpool		
Gross Tonnage	3,111	3,112	3,113

John Bibby returned in the spring of 1869 with an order for a further three ships. However, due to a slight mix up with the recording of the order, Yard Number 69 was inadvertently allocated to the *Historian*, a vessel ordered by T&J Harrison Limited. This embarrassment aside, the order was most welcome and provided a lucrative profit of £8,553 on the *Bavarian* from a selling price of £51,663. The profit realised on the other two vessels was not so significant but at £3,578 and £2,988 respectively, these orders were very gladly received.

For the construction of these three vessels Bibby had returned to the hugely successful 'Belfast bottom', or 'Bibby coffin' as it was irreverently known. The hull form had performed beyond expectations and it was decided to incorporate some new features into the design of these vessels. Internally, an additional 'tween deck divided the length of the hold into three separate cargo decks and ran the entire length of the vessel. In addition to this development, it was decided to construct the midships deckhouse as a tiered structure, with two decks above the main deck and a steering position on the top of the deckhouse. This novel design provided, for the first time, bridge wings which allowed the officer in charge to walk from the steering position to the side of the vessel while at the same time remaining in contact with the coxwain who was actually steering. This arrangement was of tremendous assistance when docking, especially in a vessel of some 400 feet in length.

In addition to these hull changes a subtle modification had been made to the engine fuelling arrangements which had the effect of increasing the cargo capacity without increasing the overall length of the vessel. By the simple addition of cross-bunkers extending across the full width of the vessel, together with the standard wing or side bunkers, the amount of coal fuel that could be carried was greatly increased without loss of cargo space. This also had the effect of increasing the operating range of the vessel between refuelling points and allowed greater flexibility of operation.

Bavarian and *Bulgarian* were broken up in 1895; *Bohemian* was wrecked and lost in 1881.

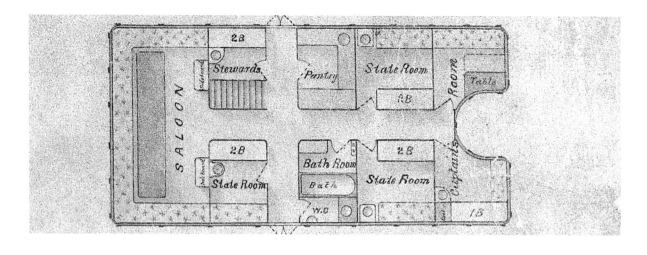

Nos 68 70 & 71
BAVARIAN. BULGARIAN. BOHEMIAN.

LENGTH of KEEL and FORERAKE	400·0
BREADTH of BEAM	37·0
DEPTH top CEILING to top SPAR DECK BEAMS	29·0
DEPTH top CEILING to top MAIN DECK BEAMS	21·5
DIAMETER of CYLINDERS 86 & 48 LENGTH of STROKE	51
GROSS REGISTER	3052·
NETT REGISTER	1982·5
BUILDERS TONNAGE	2751

— Scale ¼ inch = 1 Foot —

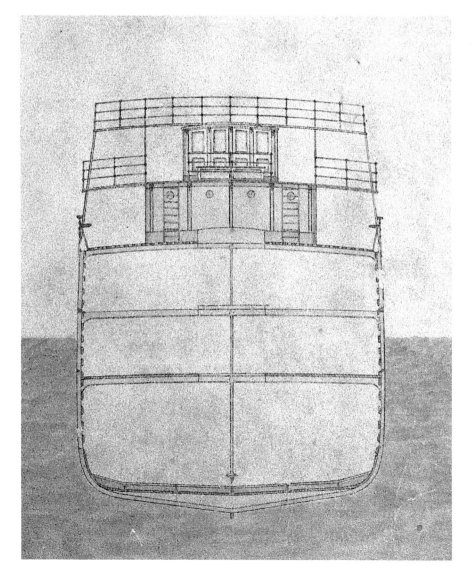

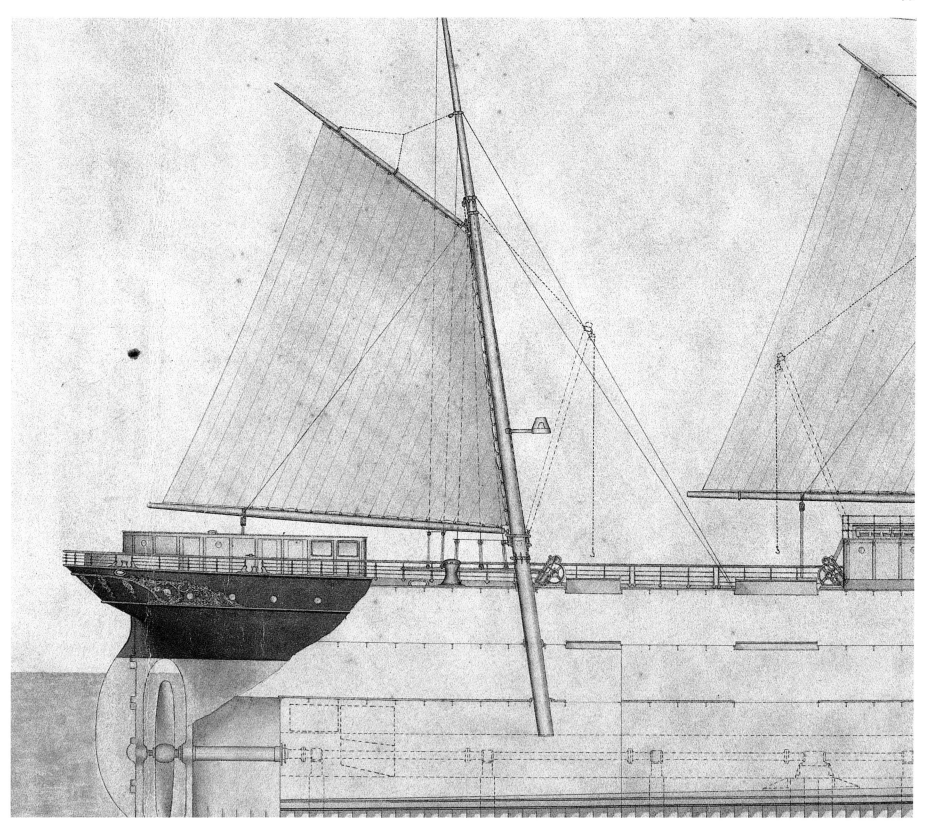

Bavarian, Bulgarian & Bohemian

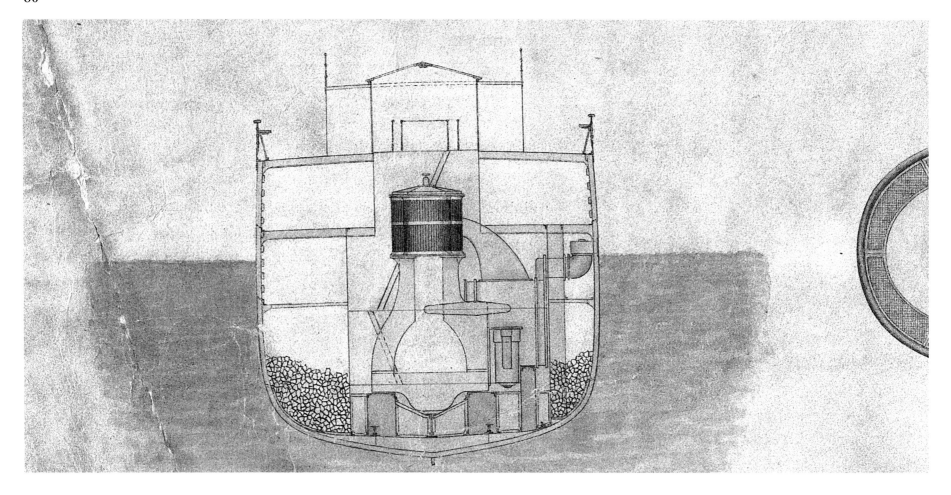

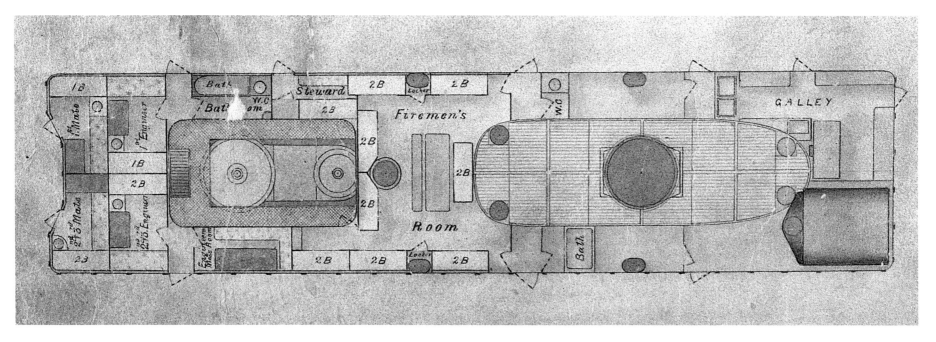

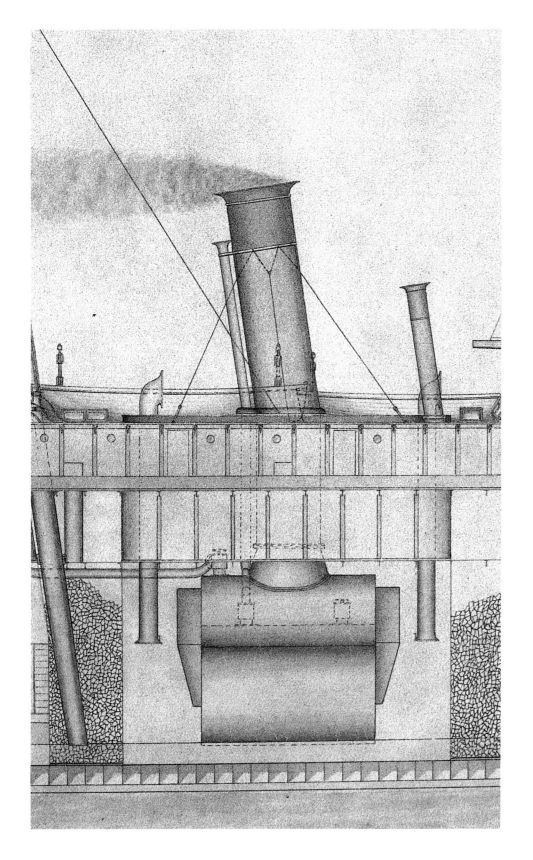

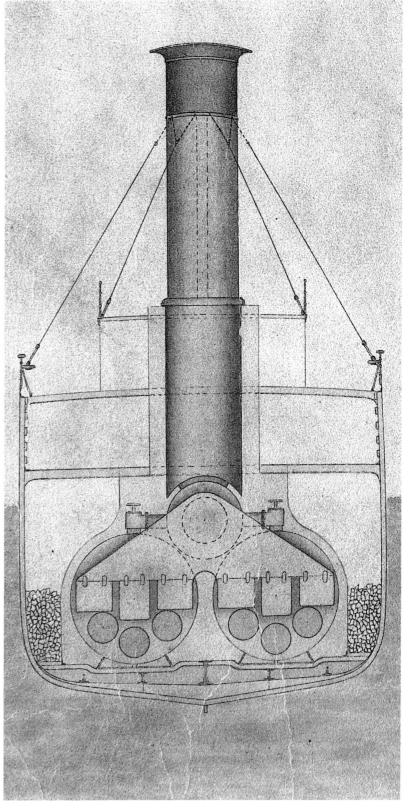

Bavarian, Bulgarian & Bohemian

Baltic

Launched 8 March 1871	Navigation Company (White Star
Delivered 2 September 1871	Line), Liverpool
Yard Number 75	**Tonnage** 3,708
Owners The Oceanic Steam	

The construction of the *Baltic* marked a further evolution in the design of merchant vessels in that she was one of the first purpose-built passenger liners and a forerunner of things to come. When Edward Harland first proposed his long and slim hull form he had also planned a new and totally novel design of passenger accommodation, one which would extend the full width of the ship and almost its entire length. With the delivery of *Baltic* he realised this ambition.

One of three sister ships, the others being the *Oceanic* and *Atlantic* (Yard Numbers 73 and 74 respectively), *Baltic* was originally to be named *Pacific;* however, White Star changed the name prior to completion. With her sisters she was designed primarily for the rapidly expanding Liverpool-New York passenger service. The opening up of the United States to the immigrant trade was a lucrative source of income to shipping companies and to retain a large slice of this market bigger and better vessels were required.

The revolutionary design of these vessels incorporated for the first time a passenger saloon or lounge that extended the full width of the vessel thus providing a large area where all passengers could dine together. A smoking room was incorporated into the accommodation replacing the usual arrangement of a canvas enclosed area on deck. Internally, the cabins were almost double the size of anything seen before and were further enhanced by the largest portholes or windows available. To power this considerable vessel White Star chose to adopt the arrangement of vertical overhead compound engines, each having a stroke of five feet. Steam was supplied by a set of seven oval single-ended boilers placed transversely across the vessel. The contract for supply of this powerful machinery was awarded to the long established company of Maudslay Sons & Field of London.

On their introduction to service the *Baltic* and her sisters received worldwide acclaim. Such was the fierce nature of the competition for the passenger trade across the Atlantic that Cunard Line immediately contracted Harland to lengthen four of its vessels and to refurbish their internal arrangements to the same standards as the White Star Line's vessels.

Baltic foundered on 6 February 1898 after striking a derelict ship that had been abandoned at sea.

BALTIC S.S.

SCALE 1 in. = 12 FEET

N° 75

LENGTH Keel & Forerake	420'·0"
BREADTH MOULDED	41'·0"
DEPTH Ton.ᵍᵉ Deck to ceiling	24'·0"
Upper Deck to D.º	32'·0"
DIAM CYLINDERS High Pressure	41"
Low Pressure	78"
LENGTH of STROKE	5'·0"
DIAM. PROPELLOR	22'·0"
BUILDERS TONNAGE	3535 $\frac{42}{94}$
NETT REG.ᵈ D.º	2218·32

Baltic

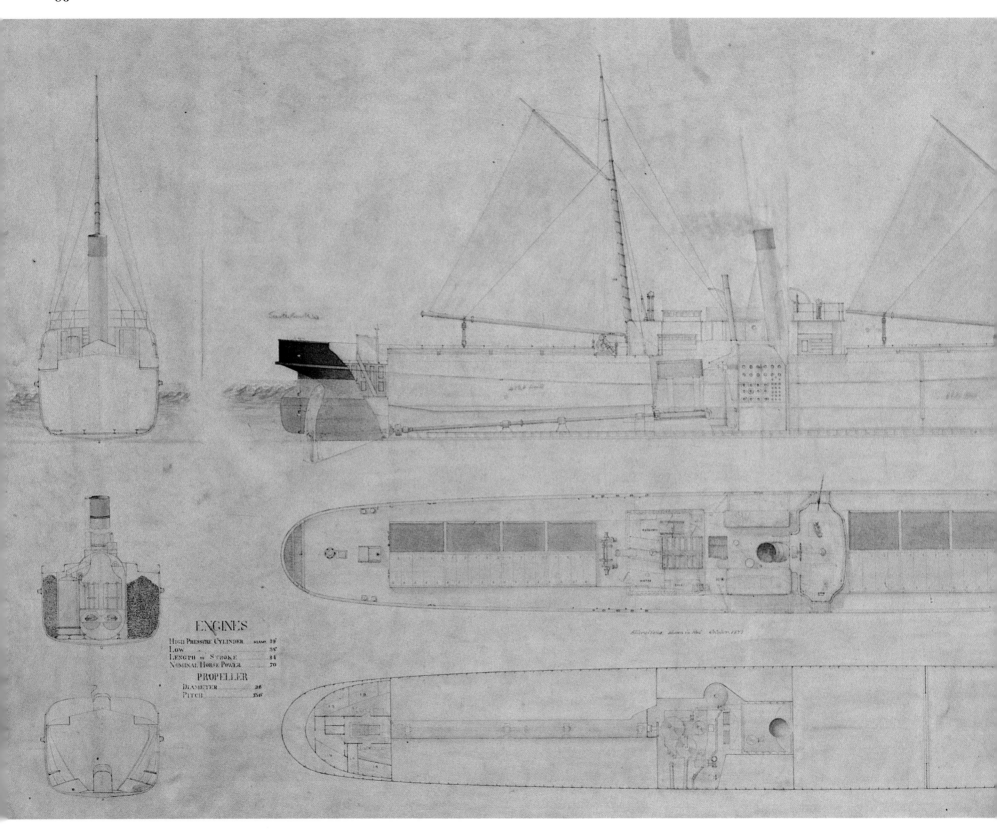

ENGINES

HIGH PRESSURE CYLINDER   DIAM. 19"
LOW   38"
LENGTH OF STROKE   24"
NOMINAL HORSE POWER   70

PROPELLER

DIAMETER   9 8
PITCH   15 0"

Camel

Launched 7 September 1870	**Owner** Harland & Wolff Limited,
Delivered 17 September 1870	Belfast
Yard Number 78	**Tonnage** 269

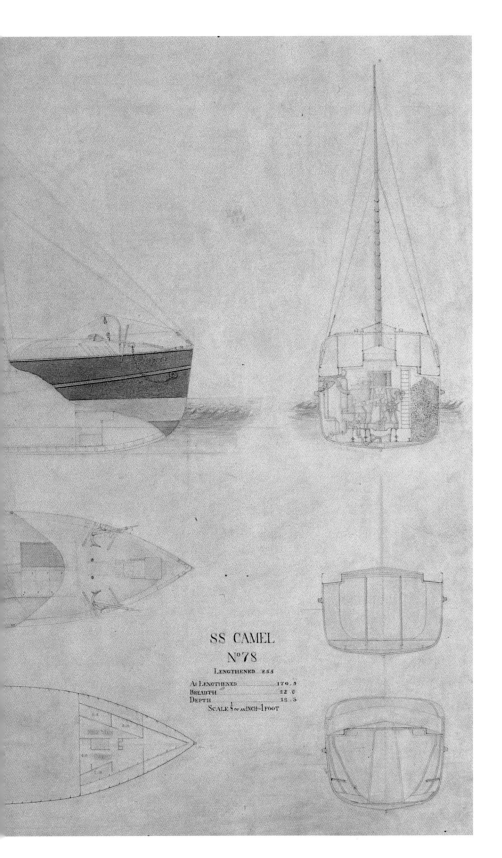

SS CAMEL
Nº 78

LENGTHENED 255

As Lengthened 170.5
Breadth 22.0
Depth 12.5
SCALE ⅛ or an INCH–1 FOOT

The construction of the *Camel* marked the entry of Harland & Wolff into the world of shipowning and vessel management on their own account. The partners had been experiencing delays in obtaining the supplies of steel and heavy machinery from the mainland, Northern Ireland having no steel or iron mills. With their shipbuilding operations rapidly expanding, such delays could, if protracted, cause major problems with construction schedules. So seriously did the partners view the situation that they decided to construct their own vessel to safeguard the company and ensure that the lifeblood of raw steel would be maintained.

The design of *Camel* reflected the specilialised nature of her intended cargo. She was fitted with two massive hatchways serving two cargo holds which themselves occupied almost the complete length of the vessel. Each hold was specially strengthened to support the weight of the iron and steel plates supplied from the rolling mills in Scotland, and was additionally designed to be as open and unclutered as possible with the minimum of internal stiffening. However, in order to achieve this it was necessary to provide *Camel* with an extra deep and specially strengthened double bottom. Motive power came from a massive seventy horsepower double-acting steam engine supplied by a set of twin water tube boilers.

During the spring of 1877 the partners decided to lengthen the vessel by twenty-five feet, the work being completed in October of that year. The result was the graceful yet workman like vessel depicted in the drawings. Accommodation was provided in a large enclosed deckhouse directly amidships with additional crew spaces at the forward and after ends of the vessel. While not now required to carry the massive engine parts to Belfast, *Camel* remained busily engaged in transporting the raw iron and steel from the Clyde.

The partners disposed of their financial interest in the vessel during a financial restructuring of the company in 1883, with the ownership of *Camel* being transferred to Gustav Wolff in partnership with two others. She was eventually sold for scrap in 1879.

SS CAMEL
Nº 78

LENGTHENED 255

AS LENGTHENED	170.5
BREADTH	22.0
DEPTH	12.3

SCALE $\frac{1}{8}$ OF AN INCH = 1 FOOT

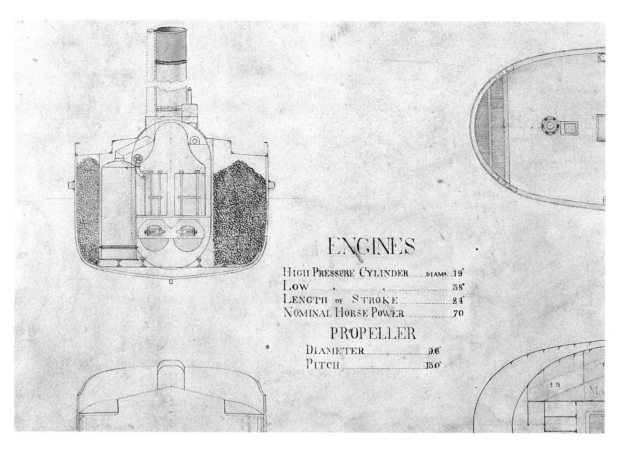

ENGINES

HIGH PRESSURE CYLINDER DIAMr.	19"
LOW	38"
LENGTH OF STROKE	24"
NOMINAL HORSE POWER	70

PROPELLER

DIAMETER	9.6"
PITCH	13.0"

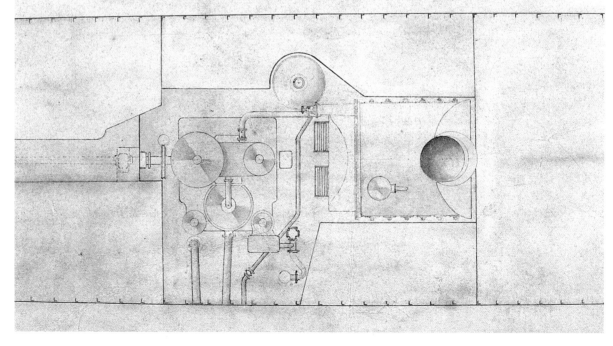

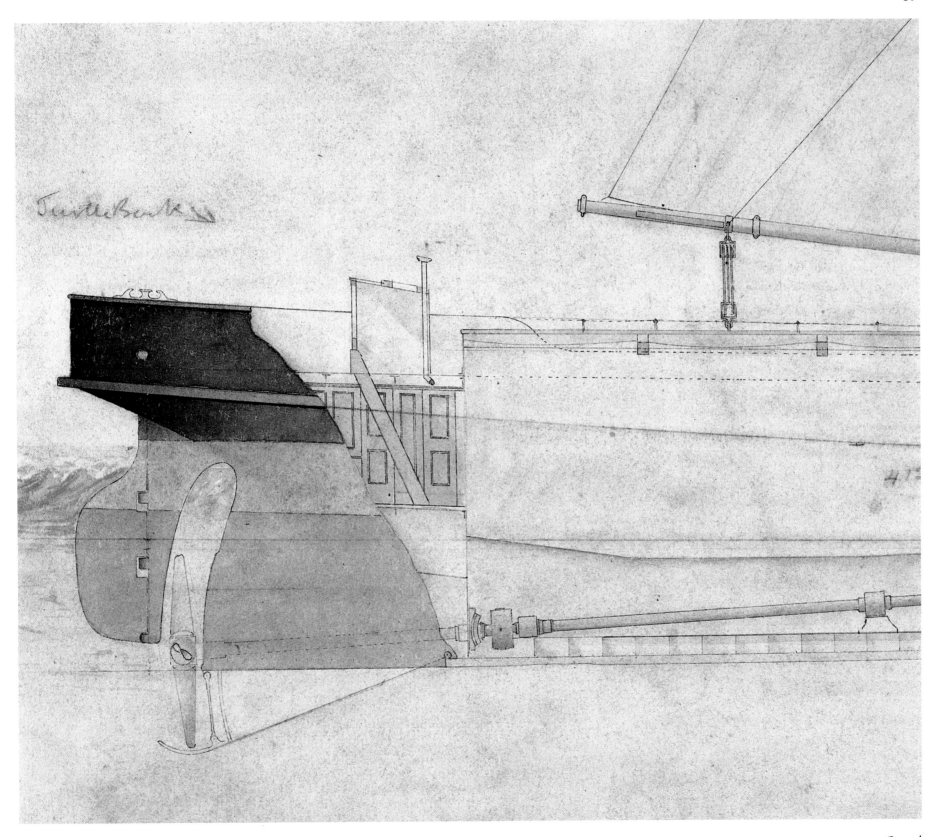

Camel

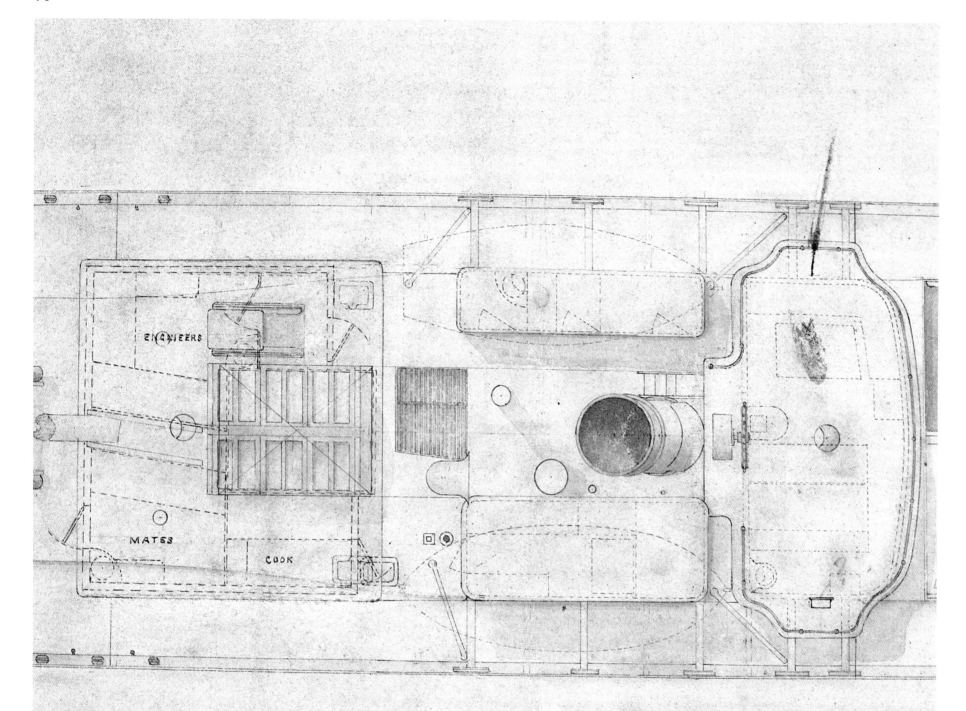

ENGINEERS

MATES

COOK

Alterations shown in Red. October. 1877

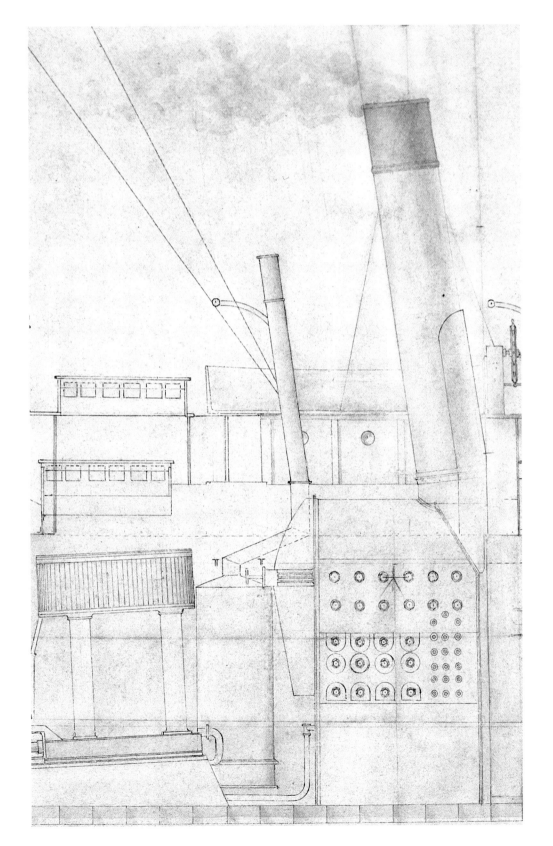

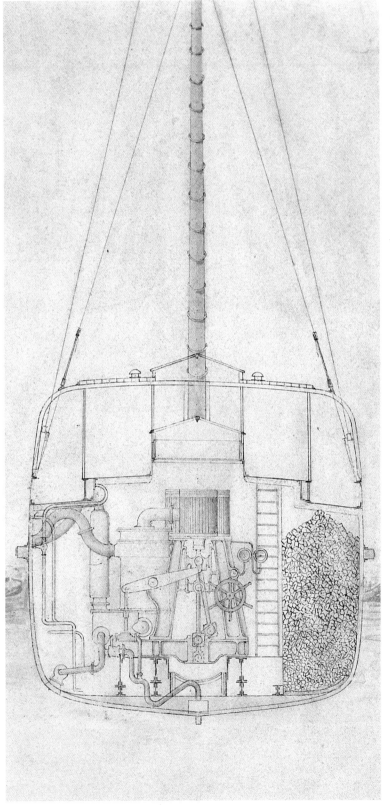

Camel

Celtic

Launched 8 June 1872
Delivered 17 October 1872
Yard Number 79
Owners Oceanic Steam Navigation Company (White Star), Liverpool
Tonnage 3,868

Originally laid down as the *Arctic*, the *Celtic* was a further adaptation and improvement on the successful design of the *Baltic*. Again designed to operate on the Liverpool-New York service, *Celtic* had a number of significant design modifications incorporated.

The successful 'all inclusive' liner concept was further developed to provide greater public lounge areas, together with a reading and writing room and an exclusive lounge for ladies. Cabin accommodation was similar to that provided on the earlier *Baltic* though White Star requested some improvements for the third class, or steerage, passengers. Previously this class of passenger was regarded almost as cargo, so much so that the usual method for them to board vessels was through open hatchways. This was to change on *Celtic* with third class passengers being provided with their own, notably separate, entrance, well away from the first and second class. However, once on board, single men and women were kept apart as much as possible, the men's cabins being forward and those for women aft; married couples were housed forward of the women's area.

A further, but unsuccessful, innovation was the provision of gas lighting throughout the vessel. This proved unreliable in service and was removed in December 1872 after *Celtic*'s fourth voyage. While steam propulsion had now become an accepted and reliable method of powering a vessel, White Star retained the traditional four masts, albeit with the sail area considerably reduced. In service, the sails were rarely used and *Celtic* found herself under tow when suffering various propulsion problems such as damaged propeller and shaft.

Sold in April 1893 to Danish shipping company Tingvalla a/s, *Celtic* found herself being broken up for scrap in France in 1898 as the *Amerika*.

Celtic

S.S. CELTIC

SCALE 1 INCH = 12 FEET

Nº 79

LENGTH KEEL & FORERAKE		437·6"
BREADTH MOULDED		41·0"
DEPTH	TON OF DECK & CEILING	23·3
	UPPER DECK to Dº	31·0"
DIAM CYLINDERS	HIGH PRESSURE	42"
	LOW Dº	78"
LENGTH OF STROKE		5·0"
DIAM PROPELLER		28·0"
BUILDERS TONNAGE		3694 Tons
NETT REGᵈ Dº		2968

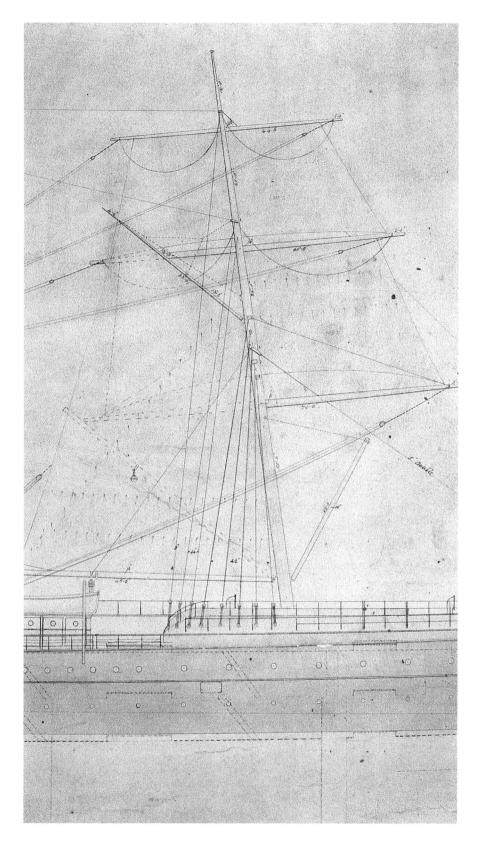

Celtic

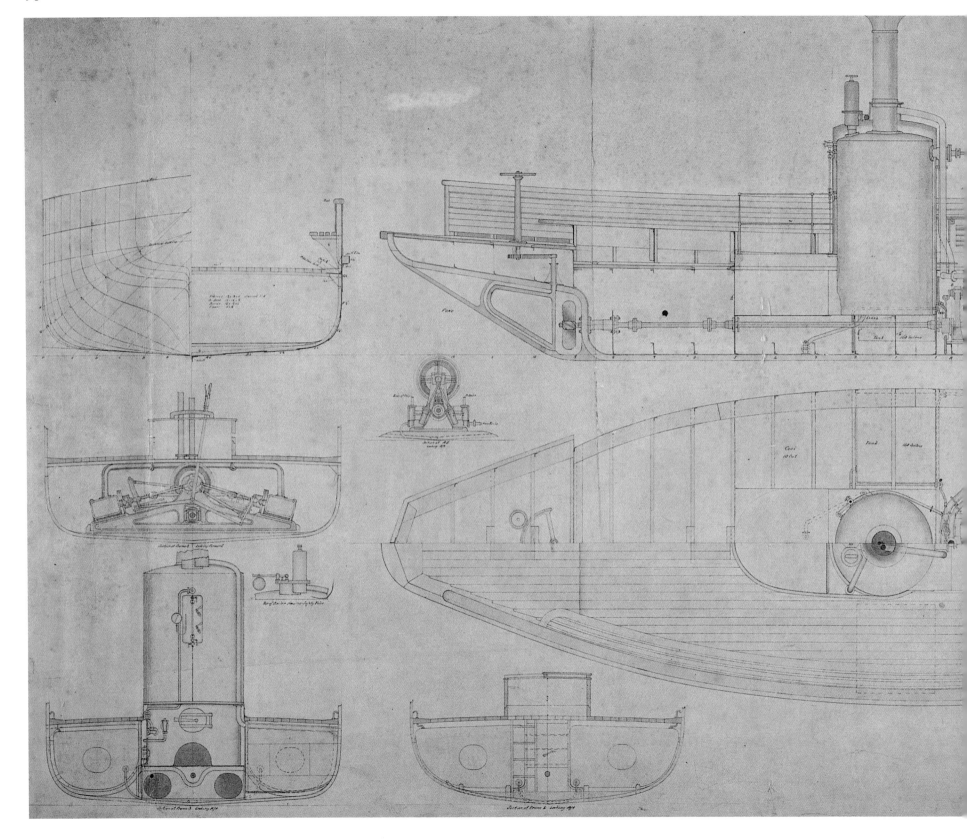

Ferry No 1

N° 8 4

Launched 25 June 1872	Owners Belfast Harbour
Delivered 1 October 1872	Commissioners
Yard Number 84	Tonnage 9

This little ferry boat, owned and operated by the Belfast Harbour Commissioners, was not considered worthy of being granted a name, yet she was a remarkably hardworking little craft.

The port of Belfast was expanding at such a pace, primarily due to the efforts of Harland & Wolff, that it soon became evident that the infrastructure surrounding the port was not keeping pace with progress. In particular, there were insufficient bridges across the River Lagan and those that existed were in the wrong place. Large numbers of workers were required to cross the river to gain access to the shipyards, and under pressure from Harland & Wolff, the harbour commissioners agreed to the construction of a river ferry to alleviate the situation. The main thrust of the argument was that Harland & Wolff could build a vessel perfectly suited to their requirements. A ferry would have the advantage of being much quicker to provide than a bridge and would be considerably cheaper. Thus *Ferry No 1* was conceived.

She was powered by a single boiler, providing steam to two single-cylinder directly opposed piston units, each in turn powering single propellers located at the forward and aft end of the vessel. Drive was engaged by a simple clutch arrangement powering a central gear wheel and operated on the principle of forward for ahead and back for astern. Classic in its simplicity, this system proved robust and reliable in all conditions. Steering was effected by twin rudders again located one at each end of the vessel and operated by a simple tiller arrangement directly attached to the rudders.

Records are not available of the eventual fate of this charming little vessel.

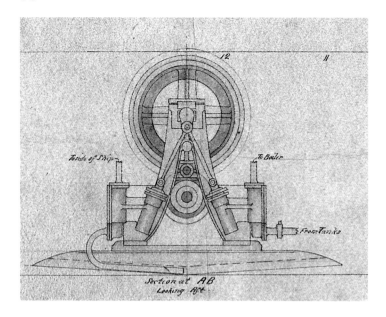

Section at AB
Looking Aft

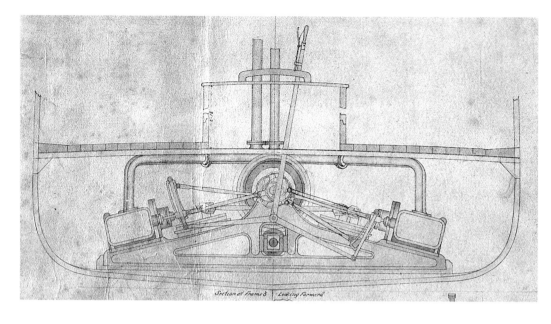

Section at Frame 5   Looking Forward

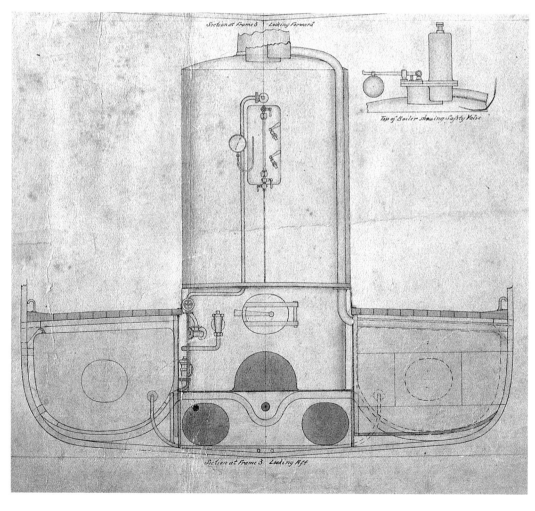

Section at Frame 5   Looking Forward

Top of Boiler showing Safety Valve

Section at Frame 5   Looking Aft

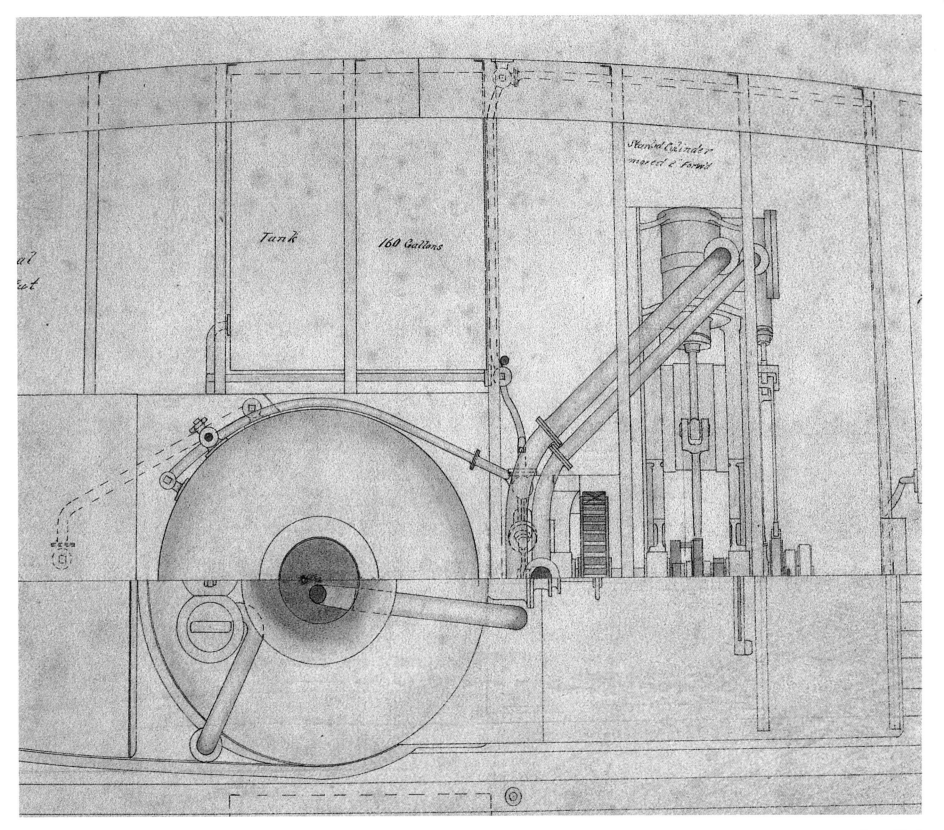

Tank

160 Gallons

Stand'd Cylinder
moved 2' forw'd

Ferry No 1

Lord Cairns

Launched 12 May 1877	**Owner** Thomas Dixon Hughes
Delivered 21 February 1878	& Company, Belfast
Yard Number 105	**Tonnage** 1335

The completion of the sailing vessel *Lord Cairns* marked a return to the traditional design of ocean going vessel. Gone were the innovative 'Belfast bottom' and steam propulsion and in their place was the standard broad beam sailing vessel of classic design. Originally ordered by the Cairn Shipping Company, the construction progressed somewhat slowly, much to the dismay of Harland & Wolff. The delays were caused by the failure of Cairn Shipping to meet the payment schedule and eventually the company went bankrupt leaving the partially completed *Lord Cairns* as a liability on the company. Work was suspended on the vessel and, with the memories of the *Broughton* still fresh, Harland & Wolff resolved to find a buyer as soon as possible: they found one in the shape of local merchants Thomas Dixon Hughes & Company.

Completed as a traditional three-masted sailing vessel, the *Lord Cairns* did, however, display some innovative features such as a large deckhouse forward of midships. However, in line with traditional design the helmsman was once again located in an open position at the aft end with the steering wheel positioned directly over the rudder. Such a simple arrangement eliminated the need for mechanical steering components and was almost foolproof in operation. Water ballast was carried in a partial double bottom with settling tanks provided at the forward and aft ends. The three large holds were equipped with portable shifting boards to ensure the safe carriage of bulk grain cargoes, each hold being served with canvas-covered hatch covers to ensure complete watertight integrity in the holds. In reality, bulk grain was only exceptionally carried with the usual cargo being bagged or bale cotton to the United Kingdom and general goods outward bound. The normal service route was all United Kingdom ports to Australia via India, the Far East and China returning via the United States west coast ports.

No 103
LORD CAIRNS.

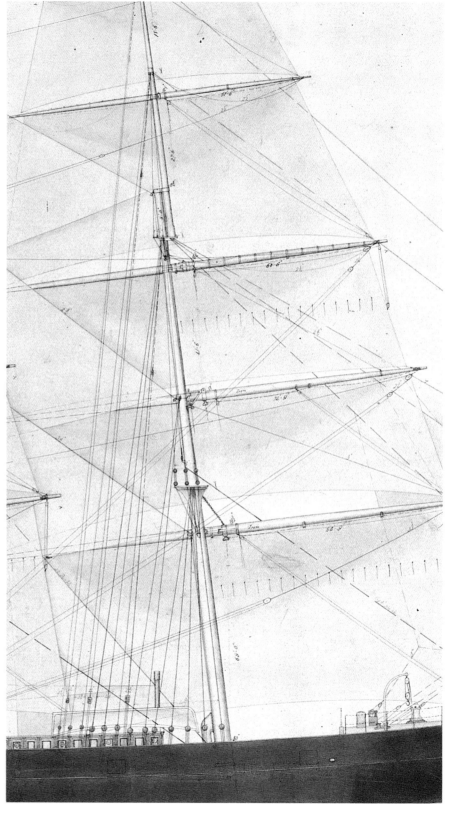

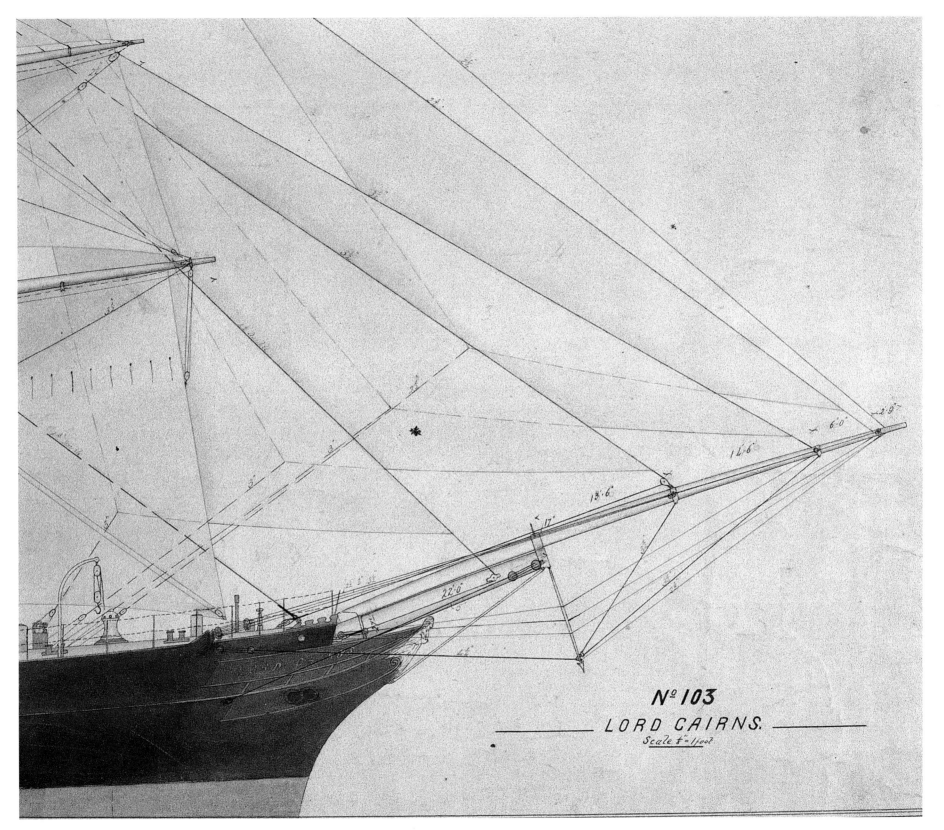

No 103

LORD CAIRNS.

Scale ⅛″ = 1 foot

Lord Cairns

Lord Cairns

N°107

LENGTH _____ 221·0"
BREADTH _____ 35·0"
DEPTH _____ 21·9"

Thurland Castle

Launched 22 July 1876	**Owners** The Lancaster
Delivered 20 September 1876	Shipowners Company, Preston
Yard Number 107	**Tonnage** 1,301

The *Thurland Castle* was again a traditional three-masted sailing vessel of classic design. Each mast was fitted with five cross arms or yards, and in addition three foresails were carried and supplemented by a sternsail. Taken together, the total sail area that could be raised was some 5,000 square feet of canvas.

The five large freeing ports on each side were a distinctive feature. These large covered openings were designed to remove sea water from the decks as rapidly as possible and operated on the 'one-way' principle – the hinged flaps forming the port covers only opened against the pressure of sea water on the deck but remained firmly closed to sea water pushing against them from outside the vessel.

Built to a four-hold design, each hold was naturally separated by the line of the masts to their base point on the tank top or double bottom. The double bottom itself was of extra depth than normal for a sailing vessel and was intended to provide a much greater degree of stiffness to the hull. Another unusual and distinctive feature of this vessel was the three stove pipes which extended from the aft end of the forward deckhouse. The larger of these pipes carried the smoke from the galley range. The other two carried away the smoke from a group of coal fires that provided a crude but effective form of central heating in the deckhouse. These comforts were enjoyed only by the officers; the crew, located as usual at the forward and aft ends below the main deck, had to fend for themselves as best they could.

Intended for worldwide service in all conditions, the *Thurland Castle* was a sturdy and well equipped vessel able to counter the extreme conditions that could be encountered around Cape Horn in particular.

Thurland Castle

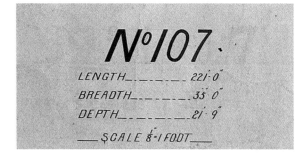

Nº 107.

LENGTH _____ 221' 0"
BREADTH _____ 35' 0"
DEPTH _____ 21' 9"

_____ SCALE ⅛=1 FOOT _____

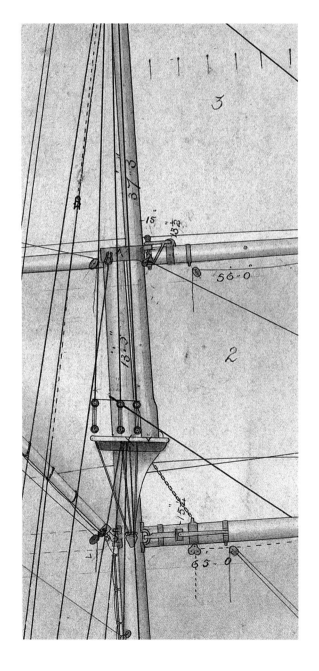

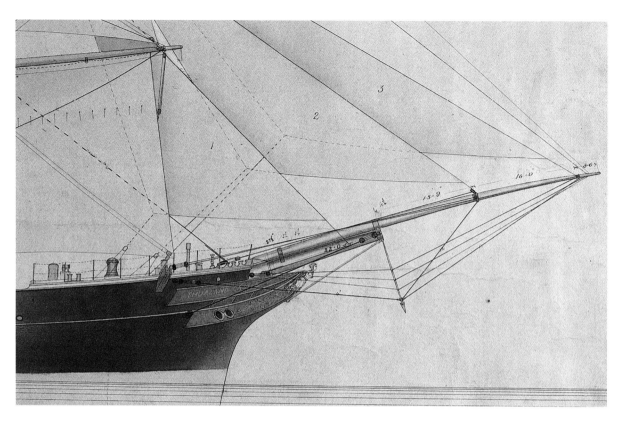

Thurland Castle

Steelfield

No 108

Length ----- 221:0
Breadth ----- 35:0
Depth ----- 21:0
Scale ¼ = 1ᶠᵗ

Launched 2 December 1876	**Owners** R C McNaughton &
Delivered 1 January 1877	Company, Belfast
Yard Number 108	**Tonnage** 1,315

With the completion of *Steelfield* a new era had begun in the carriage of passengers across the Atlantic and to the gold fields of Australia. Shipowners still required vessels to be designed primarily for the carriage of cargo, but the ever-increasing flow of passengers, usually regarded as little better than cargo themselves, had to be furnished with accommodation which provided a greater degree of consideration than that afforded to their predecessors.

Harland & Wolff had always maintained an active interest in the developments taking place in the shipping world. In all likelihood this interest was driven by the relationship between Wolff and his uncle Gustav Schawbe, who had various business interests in several shipping companies. In any event, to have a good knowledge of developments can only be beneficial to a shipbuilder: it ensures that their vessel designs are as up to date as possible and anticipate future requirements. This set of circumstances, therefore, was the driving force behind the development of the *Steelfield* and other similar vessels.

Conceived as a clipper ship and posessing the classic hull form for the type, *Steelfield* was, however, radically different in her internal accommodation arrangement. Passengers were no longer simply emigrants for whom little in the way of creature comforts were provided. A rising number of passengers demanded luxury and, more importantly for the shipowner, could afford to pay for it. For *Steelfield*, Harland & Wolff set new standards in passenger facilities with the introduction of a 'saloon' class of accommodation which, as the name implies, simply referred to the dining arrangement. Usually passengers were provided with meals in a communal dining room; this more affluent class of passenger was permitted to dine at the captain's table in the officers' saloon. In addition, they would be accommodated in private cabins and provided with bedding, clean linen and fresh water for washing (everyone else, apart from the officers, had to use seawater). The cost of such luxury, however, did come at a considerable price in 1876. A one way passage to the east coast ports of the United States would cost £30 per person and £63 to Australia. In comparison, the emigrant fare for the same journeys would be £7.10 shillings and £16. 16 shillings.

Innovative for the time, *Steelfield* proved a popular and reliable vessel; however, her career was not destined to be a lengthy one in passenger terms. The rapid developments in steam power and its increased reliability caused shipowners and passengers alike to demand ever larger and faster vessels. The era of the pure sailing ship was rapidly drawing to a close and, after only twelve years in service, deserted by her passengers for the lure of the new steamships, *Steelfield* had her passenger accommodation removed and the space returned to the carriage of cargo. She was eventually sold for scrap in 1894.

№ 108

Length ——— 221'·0"
Breadth ——— 35'·0"
Depth ——— 21'·0"
————— Scale ⅛"=1ᶠᵗ —————

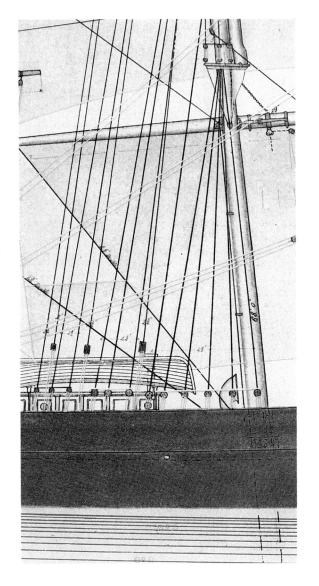

Steelfield

SCHOONER YACHT "GLADYS"
Nº 109

LENGTH
BREADTH
TONNAGE
Do
Do

SCALE

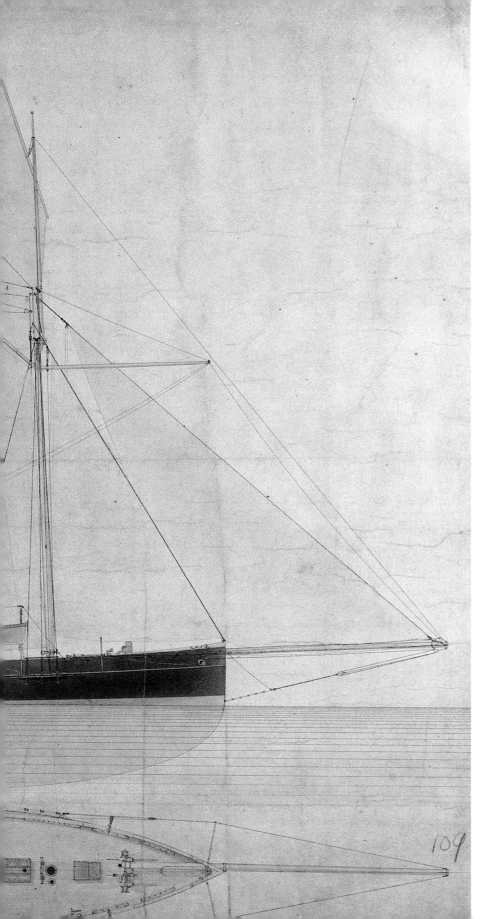

Gladys

Launched 11 May 1876	**Owner** Mr N Mathieson, London
Delivered 23 May 1876	**Tonnage** 52
Yard Number 109	

From her snub nose all the way aft to her raised and upswept stern, the schooner type yacht *Gladys* was distinctive of her class. Even today sailing yachts which display this characteristic stern are known as schooners.

Designed for speed and named after her owner's daughter, *Gladys* incorporated a very deep hull extending downward in sweeping curves to a narrow keel. From here, to the top of the gaf-rigged masts, *Gladys* displayed her pedigree as a sailing yacht of classic proportions, with an overall length of eighty two feet complementing the moulded or shaped breadth of fifteen feet eight inches.

Equipped with three glass-covered hatchways leading down to the accommodation below, the whole impression was one of light and space. The traditional steering wheel was dispensed with in preference of a single arm tiller arrangement extending forward from the raised stern deck. At the forward end a side anchor fitted with a quick release mechanism was located on the starboard side close to the twin mooring and anchor windlasses. The lines of the vessel exuded grace and elegance, coupled with a sense of speed and purpose. Sadly, no record exists of how or when the *Gladys* finally ended her days.

116

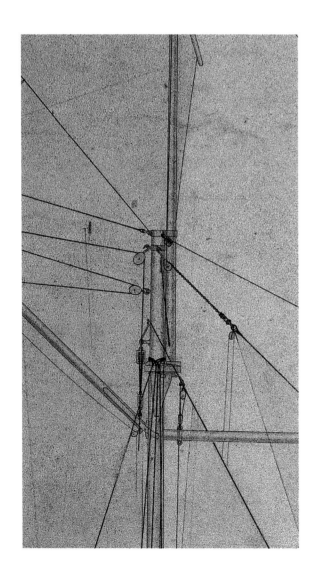

SCHOONER YACHT "GLADYS"
Nº 109

LENGTH	for Tonnage	79·8
BREADTH	Extreme	15·8
TONNAGE	Yacht measurement	85¾
Do	Builders	91⁶⁶⁄₉₄
Do	Board of Trade	51⁷⁸⁄₁₀₀

SCALE ⅛IN=1FT

Gladys

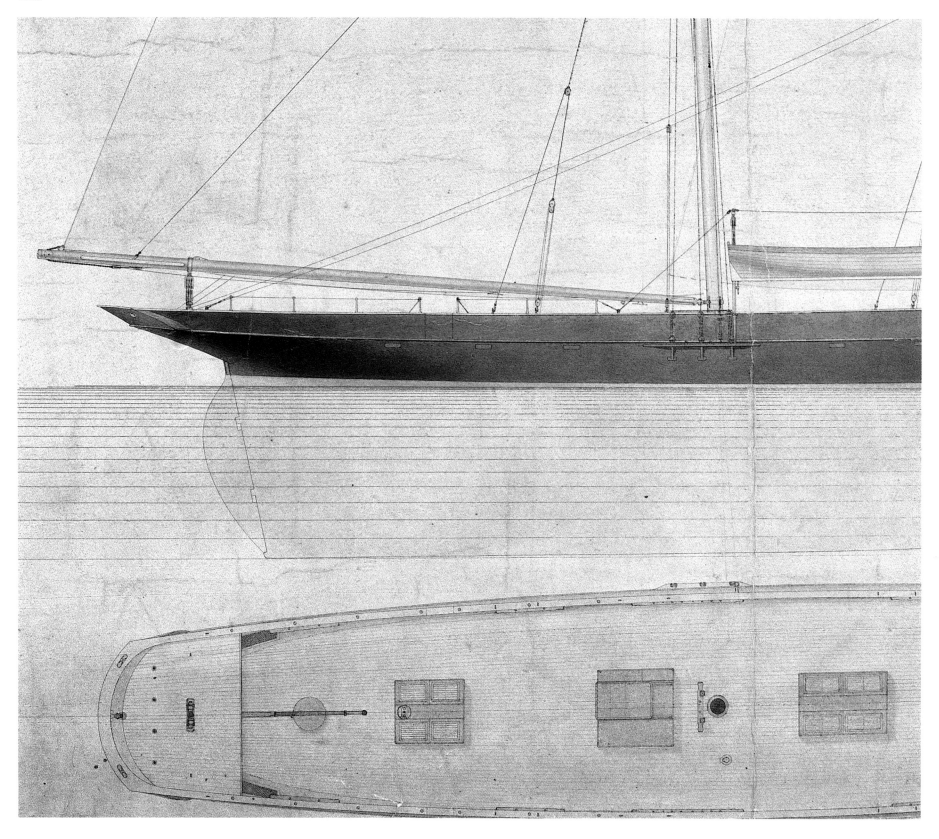

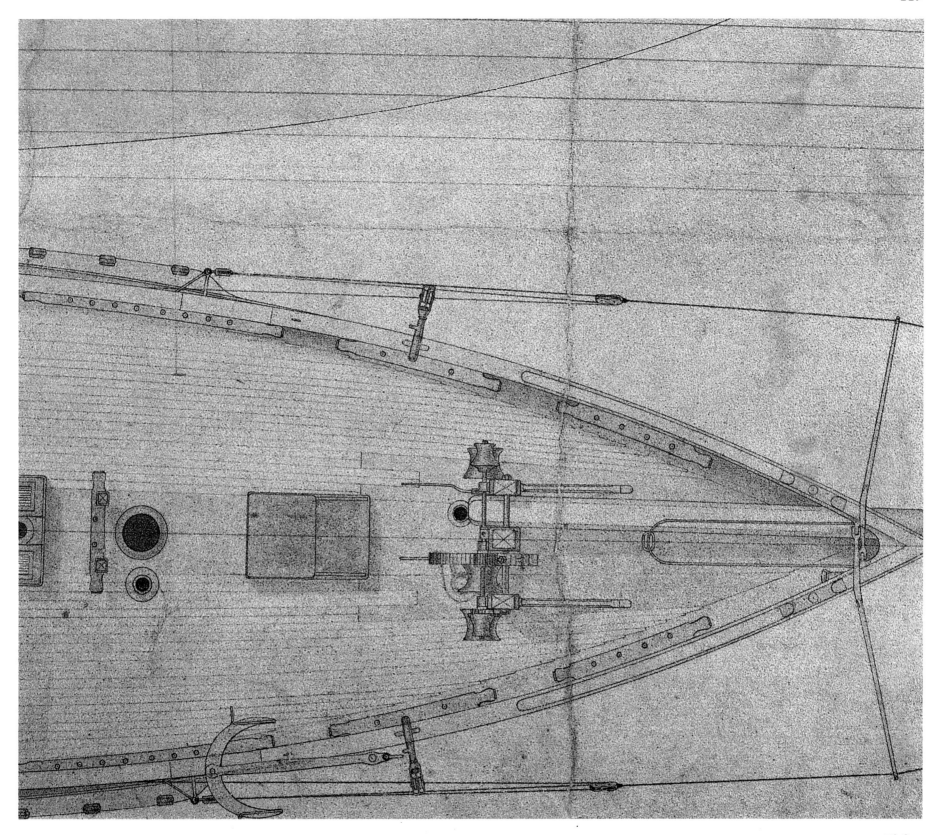

Gladys

Slieve More, Slieve Bawn & Slieve Roe

	Slieve More	Slieve Bawn	Slieve Roe
Launched	10 February 1877	31 March 1877	2 February 1878
Delivered	24 March 1877	12 May 1877	16 March 1878
Yard No	110	111	115
Owners	W J Sinclair & Co, Liverpool		
Tonnage	1,749	1,749	1,749

In 1876 Harland & Wolff had agreed to two additional partners joining the board of the company – W H Wilson, a well known and innovative engineer, and W J Pirrie, who had several business interests. In agreeing to this expansion, the original partners were shrewdly laying the foundations for the continued success of their business empire. These seeds were soon to bear fruit in an order for three jute clippers for W J Sinclair & Company which, not surprisingly, was managed by none other than William Pirrie Sinclair, a cousin of W J Pirrie.

In order to secure such a valuable contract, the partners returned to their well tried formula of retaining a share in the vessels, with Edward Harland himself holding the largest stake of £3,000 per vessel. This was a considerable investment for one person at that time, especially when compared to a building cost of £26,400 per vessel.

Constructed to the standard sailing ship hull form, these otherwise unremakable vessels provided their owners with sterling service in the carriage from India of jute bound for cotton mills in the north of England; on their outward journeys they carried finished cloth. Their slab-sided appearance presented an unattractive profile, yet this choice of hull form was entirely functional and consistent with the carriage of the heavy and bulky jute cargo.

Slieve More, Slieve Brawn & Slieve Row

122

Nᵒˢ 110, 111 & 115
SLIEVE MORE, SLIEVE BAWN & SLIEVE ROE.
RIGGING PLAN
Scale ⅜" to 1foot

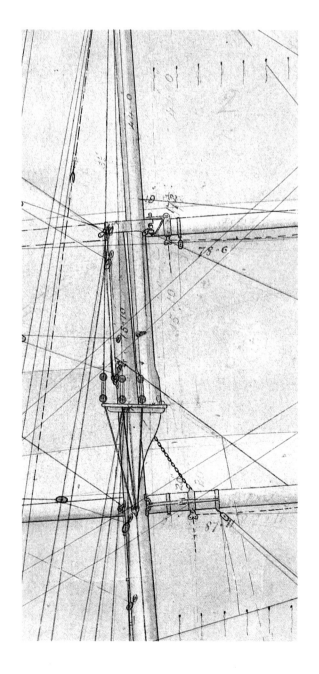

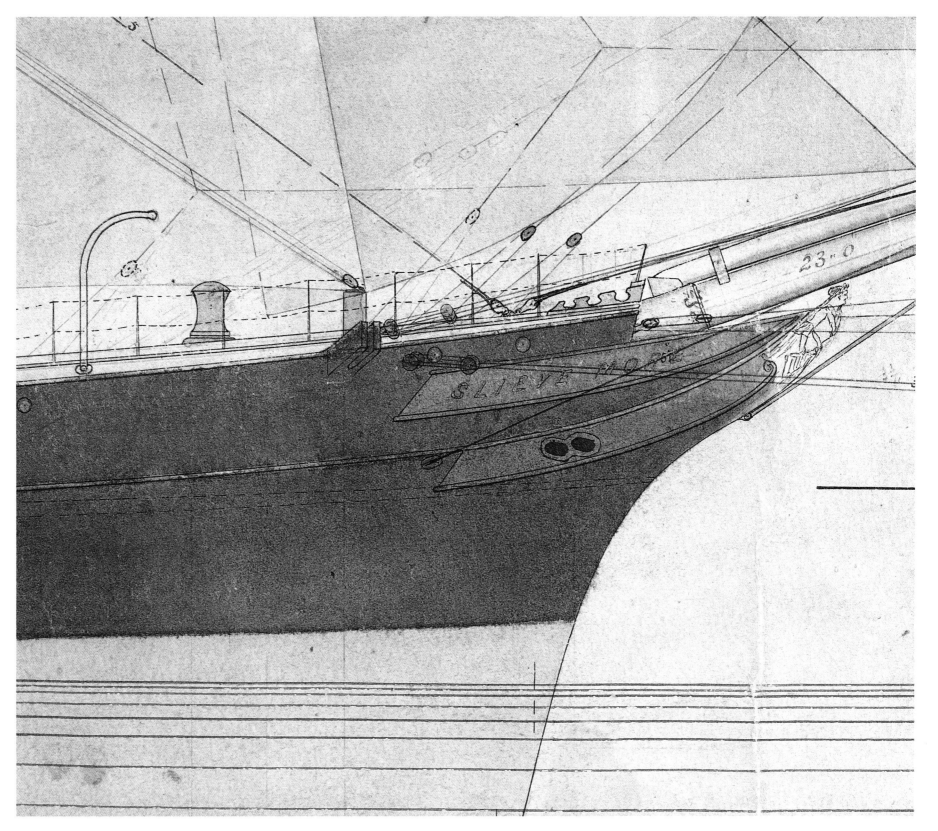

Slieve More, Slieve Brawn & Slieve Row

Star of Italy & Star of France

N⁰ˢ 113 & 114

STAR of ITALY & STAR of FRAN...

LENGTH .... 250 . 0
BREADTH .... 38 . 0
DEPTH .... 22 . 9

— SCALE ⅜ FOOT —

	Star of Italy	*Star of France*
Launched	26 July 1877	21 November 1877
Delivered	18 October 1877	5 January 1878
Yard Number	113	114
Owners	J P Corry & Company, Belfast	
Tonnage	1,644	1,663

Designed for the India (Calcutta) and Australian service of J P Corry, these magnificent sailing clippers embodied the most up to date facilities of any comparable vessel of the period, and were indicative of the class of passenger they served. In 1887, the British Empire covered almost half of the globe, with perhaps the most notable possession being India. This colonial influence was most evident in the number of high-ranking government officials, army officers and their families taking passage to India. Consequently, the standard of vessel operating on this route had to reflect the status and elegance of its passengers. The *Star of Italy* and her sister *Star of France* were conceived with just such a class of passenger in mind and accordingly their accommodation set new and unprecedented standards of luxury.

The internal decoration of the saloon accommodation was finished in the most ornate and elegantly carved mahogany panelling with large settees and chairs covered in damask and velvet upholstery. The main saloon was situated in a large deckhouse just aft of the foremast and along the centre line of the the vessel, the position being chosen in order to minimise the effects of pitching and rolling in heavy seas. Opening off from this magnificent room were four extra large staterooms designed to accommodate families. Additional two-bedded cabins were located at the stern of the vessel under the poop deck, being reached from a private carved mahogany staircase. All cabins had a bath and wash hand basin supplied with fresh water from tanks located in the double bottom. Above these cabins was the steering position located in a small deckhouse which afforded some shelter from the elements.

Meals were prepared in the large galley which was located below and aft of the main saloon – interesting features here being the metal lined ceiling, walls and ceramic tiled floor to prevent the spread of fire. At the forward end was the crew accommodation, which comprised of four and eight-berth cabins and a communal dining area. Lighting throughout the vessel was provided by oil lamps mounted on gimbals to ensure they remained upright.

Being iron vessels, the hulls were constructed on the 'joggle' principle, with each row (or 'strake') of plating being 'joggled' – overlapped – for the full height of the vessel, the first row being overlapped on the outside by the second row. The third row was then located behind the second row and so on producing an in-and-out effect.

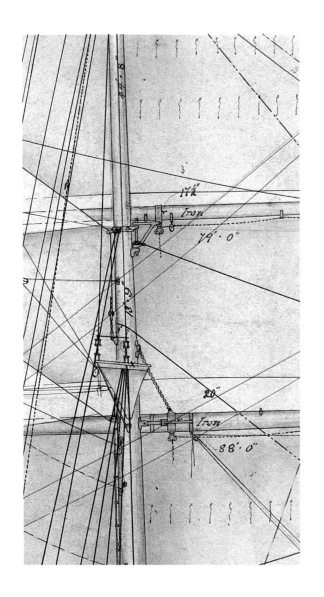

N⁰ˢ 113 & 114

STAR OF ITALY & STAR OF FRANCE

LENGTH _____ 250 . 0
BREADTH _____ 38 . 0
DEPTH _____ 22 . 9

SCALE ⅛=1 FOOT

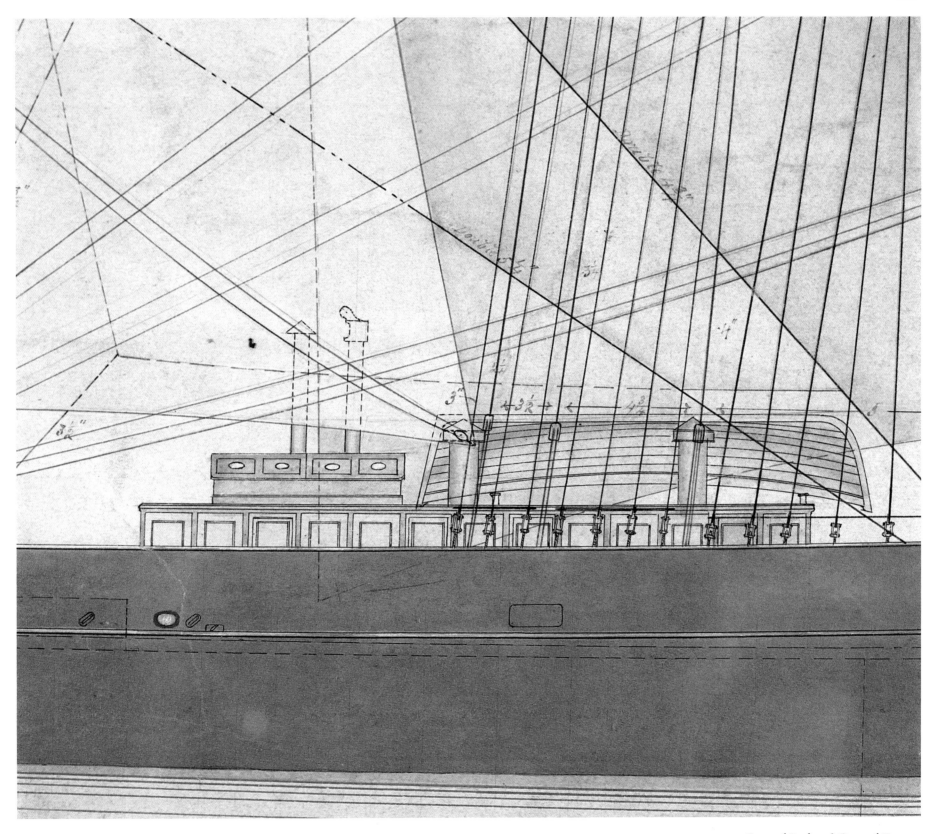

Star of Italy & Star of France

Star of Italy & Star of France

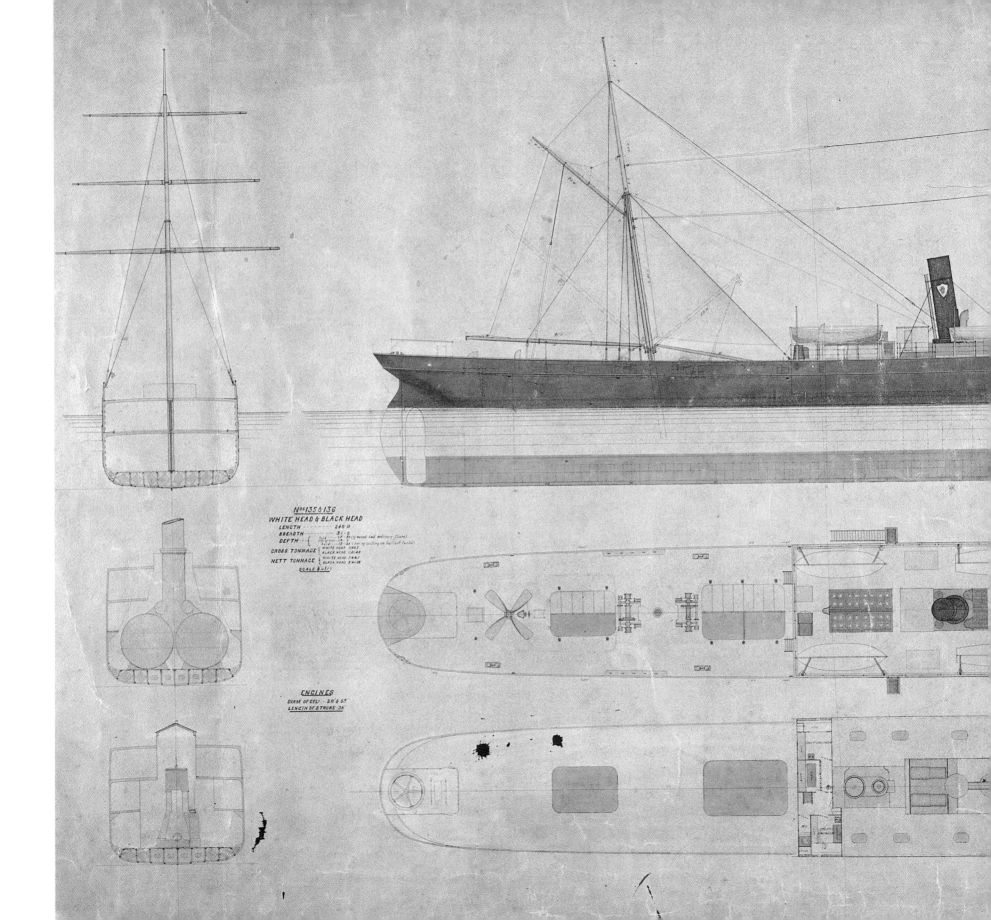

Nos 135 & 136
WHITE HEAD & BLACK HEAD
LENGTH ------- 240 II
BREADTH ------- 31 6
DEPTH ---
CROSS TONNAGE
NETT TONNAGE
SCALE

ENGINES
DIAM of CYL - 29 & 53
LENGTH of STROKE 36

White Head & Black Head

	White Head	*Black Head*
Launched	5 May 1880	15 January 1881
Delivered	21 January 1881	14 March 1881
Yard Number	135	136
Owners	Ulster Steamship Company, Belfast	
Tonnage	1,192	1,191

White Head and *Black Head* were built to the order of George Heyn & Company for their Canadian service to all ports along the St Lawrence river. Principally engaged in the carriage of general goods from British and Irish ports, these magnificent vessels were purpose-designed for their task and incorporated a number of inventive design features.

A spare cast iron propeller was carried on a special cradle at the aft end and was capable of being fitted to the vessel without the necessity for dry docking. In order to accomplish this operation, water ballast was pumped out from the aft tanks while sequentially flooding the forward ballast compartments. This had the effect of raising the stern of the vessel clear of the water, thus facilitating removal and replacement of the propeller. This simple innovation produced considerable savings in time and docking charges. A further development was the upward slope of the lower bow, designed to ride up and crush the ice frequently found on the St Lawrence in winter and thus extending the operational window for the vessel.

While originally fitted with sails on the fore and main masts, these were of little practical use and were later discarded altogether. Passenger accommodation was provided in an enclosed midships structure surmounted by an open bridge. The general crew quarters were located at the forward end under the forecastle deck.

The Ulster Steamship Company, or Head Line as it was known, operated until 1976 when it was eventually forced to close due to commercial pressures. The company, however, retains a shipping and travel agency business today. It is interesting to note that the construction of these two vessels was undertaken at a loss of over thirteen percent of the actual building cost of £63,000 per vessel: by accepting these lossses, Harland & Wolff Limited were, in effect, storing up trouble which would return to haunt them in the years ahead.

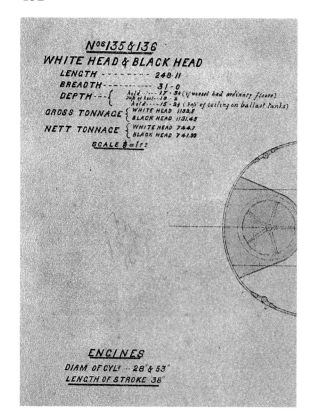

Nᵒˢ 135 & 136

WHITE HEAD & BLACK HEAD

LENGTH --------- 248·11
BREADTH --------- 31·0
DEPTH --- { hold ---- 17·3¾ (if vessel had ordinary floors)
top of keel-- 19·2
hold ---- 15·2¾ (top of ceiling on ballast tanks)
GROSS TONNAGE { WHITE HEAD 1192·5
BLACK HEAD 1191·45
NETT TONNAGE { WHITE HEAD 744·7
BLACK HEAD 741·99

SCALE ⅛ = 1 f ²

ENGINES

DIAM OF CYLˢ --- 28" & 53"
LENGTH OF STROKE 38"

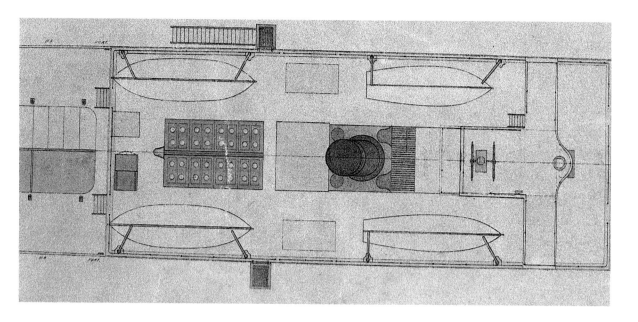

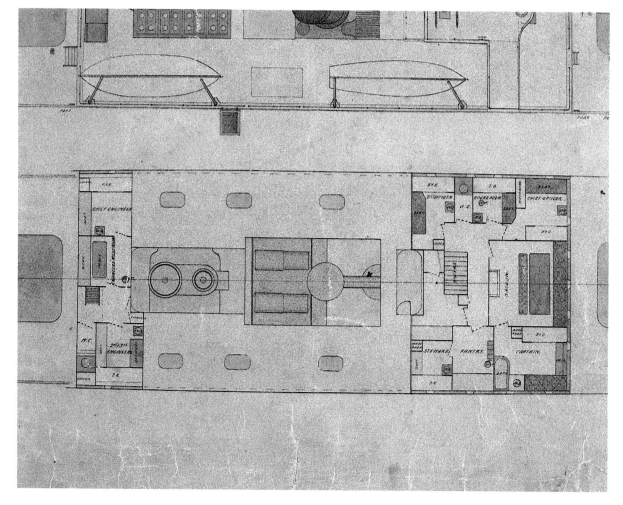

132

White Head & Black Head

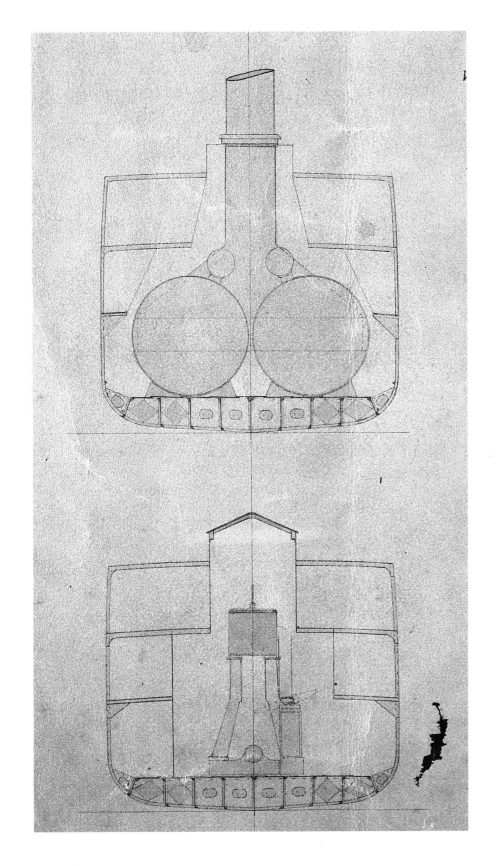

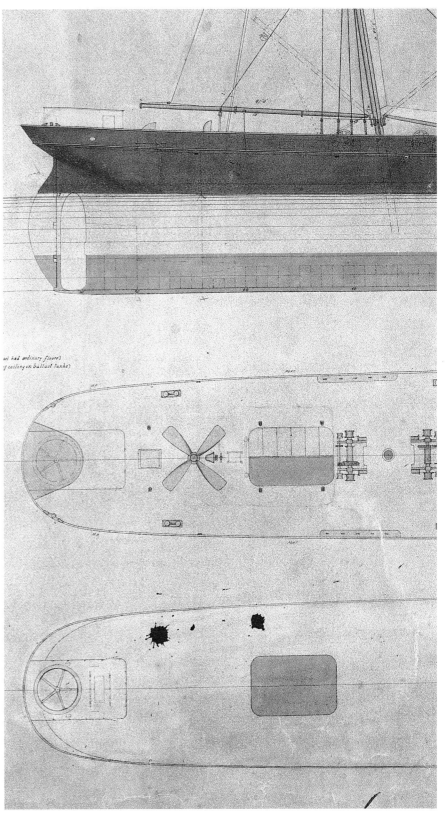

White Head & Black Head

British Queen
& British King

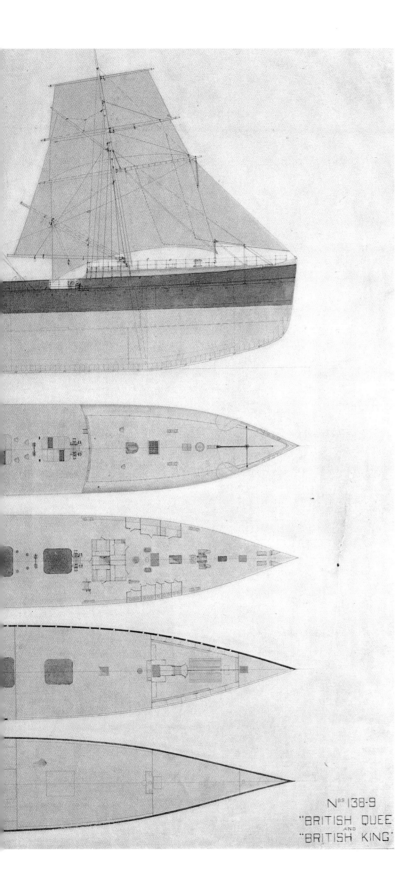

N⁰ˢ 138-9
"BRITISH QUEE
AND
"BRITISH KING"

	British Queen	*British King*
Launched	4 November 1880	22 January 1880
Delivered	15 January 1881	29 March 1881
Yard Numbers	138	139
Owners	Ulster Steamship Company, Belfast	
Tonnage	3,558	3,559

The building of the *British Queen* and *British King* heralded yet another innovation for Harland & Wolff. These two vessels were the first all passenger ships to be constructed by the company. They also marked a radical change from the use of iron, the traditional construction material of shipbuilding, and employed steel for the first time in the hull construction. Steel had been available for many years although, in tests, it had proved too brittle to be of any practical use for shipbuilding. Now, with the development of the 'Bessemer' process, steel shipbuilding became technically possible for the first time. The new steel plates could be provided at much larger sizes than were available in iron and, with its greater tensile strength, it did not need to be as thick as iron plating. The modern passenger liners of today are built using the same technology as Harland & Wolff's pioneering *British Queen* and *British King*.

Comprising of four full-length internal decks, almost all of this space could be utilised for passenger accommodation. With space no longer at a premium, grand areas were available to voyagers for socialising, entertainment and communal dining areas. Transportation of cargo was not abandoned entirely however, and the lower deck, from the double bottom to the first internal deck, were given over to hold space. Four small hatches, which were trunked through the decks to the lower level, allowed access for cargo operations; although the size of cargo items carried was governed by the dimensions of the hatch entrance.

The engines were placed exactly in the centre of the vessel to minimise the vibration emanating from the massive cranks and pistons. This arrangement, while benefitting passenger comfort, created a set of operational difficulties for both the shipbuilder and the operator. To allow smooth rotation of the propeller shaft, which ran for almost half the length of the vessel, extreme care was taken to ensure that it was completely parallel to the hull bottom. This complex operation required that the shaft be supported on several 'Plummer' (or thrust) blocks, and each section of shaft had to be carefully balanced. Sails were again installed but were primarily for aesthetic purposes as they were of little practical use.

British Queen was torpedoed and sunk in the English Channel on 30 August 1918. *British King* was scuttled by the Russians at Port Arthur in March 1904.

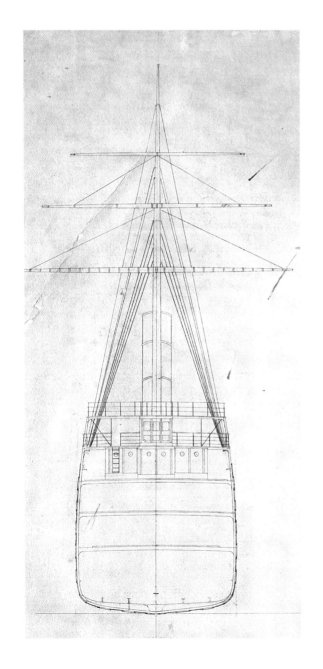

N⁰ˢ 138-9
"BRITISH QUEEN"
AND
"BRITISH KING"

British Queen & British King

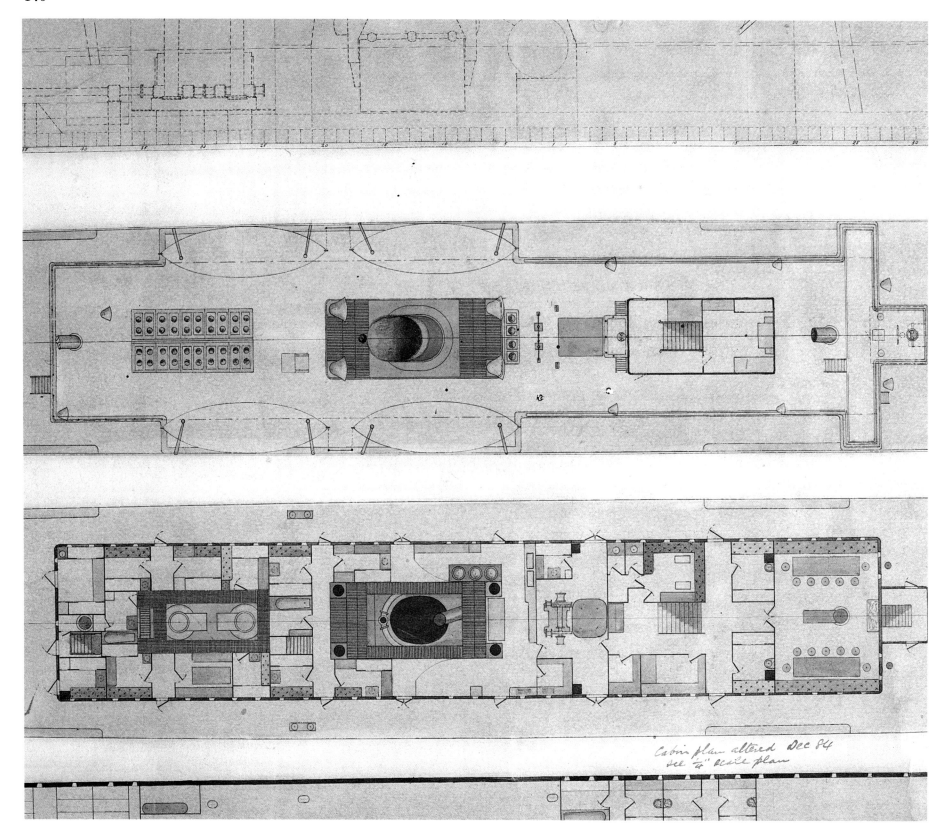

Cabin plan altered Dec 84
see ¼" scale plan

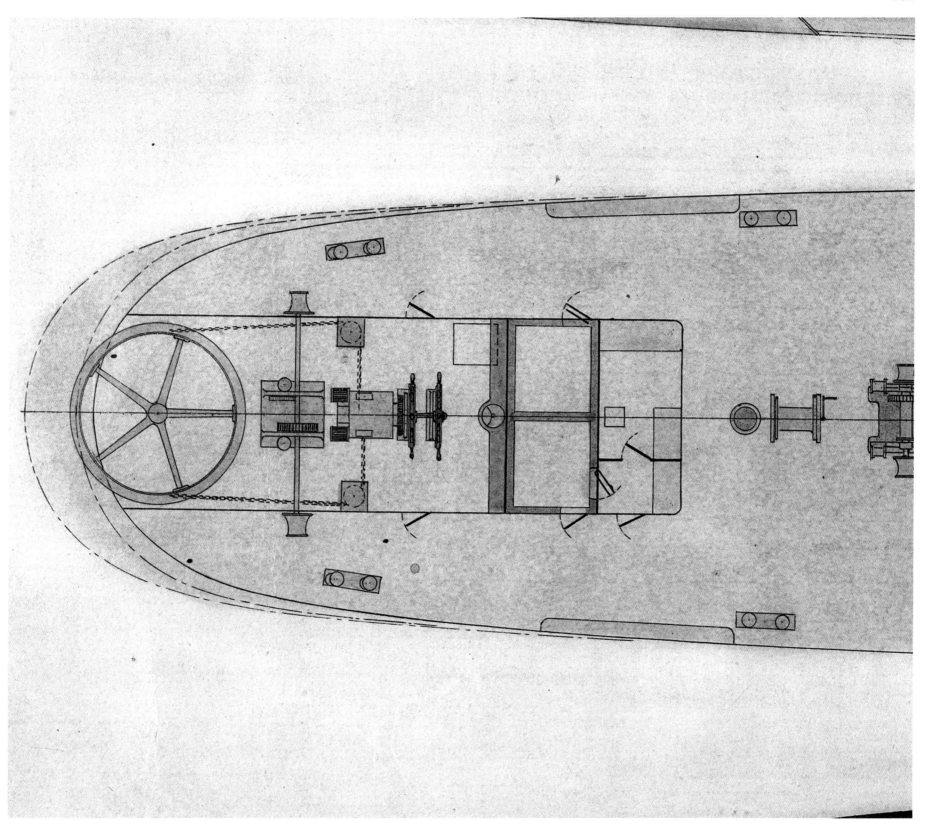

British Queen & British King

S.S. "ARABIC" & "COPTIC"

Arabic & Coptic

	Arabic	Coptic
Launched	30 April 1881	10 August 1881
Delivered	12 August 1881	9 November 1881
Yard Numbers	141	142
Owners	Oceanic Steam Navigation Company (White Star Line), Liverpool	
Tonnage	4,368	4,448

The *Arabic* was originally laid down as the *Asiatic*; however, as had occurred on several previous occasions, the White Star Line apparently suffered from great indecision when deciding on a suitable name. Frequent changes of this kind resulted in confusion and frustration for the shipbuilder, but their reliance on the owner for return business dictated that such inconveniences had to be accepted with good grace.

Arabic and *Coptic* were designed for the White Star transatlantic routes; however, the operations of these two vessels were slightly more unusual than other ships in the fleet. While accommodating the normal mixture of steerage and more affluent passengers, they were also specifically designed to carry another lucrative passenger; one that did not require the various trappings of comfort and who did not complain about the food or service. The export of live cattle was now a major source of income for the shipping lines who saw no problem in mixing the human cargo with its bovine equivalent.

The lower holds were given over exclusively to housing the cattle, and the animals were tended by a gang of specially trained stockmen whose duties were to ensure that food and water were available and the cattle sludge removed. This latter process was accomplished by the simple expedient of shovelling the waste into buckets and discharging it directly into the sea. Complaints from human passengers, particurlarly those in steerage, whose accommodation was directly over the cattle pens, regarding the noise and smell were mostly ignored. Needless to say, these ships very seldom carried first class passengers and the official classification of this type of vessel was 'intermediate', as they were somewhere between pure cargo vessels and passenger liners.

Arabic was scrapped at Preston in August 1901; *Coptic* was scrapped at Osaka in 1926.

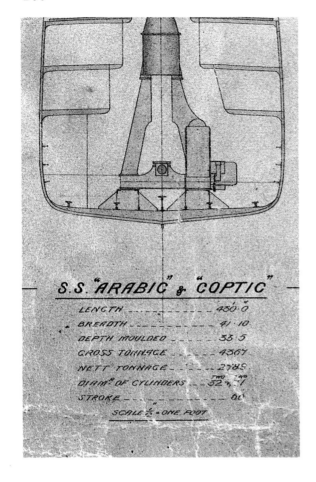

S.S. "ARABIC" & "COPTIC"

LENGTH	430·0
BREADTH	41·10
DEPTH MOULDED	33·5
GROSS TONNAGE	4367
NETT TONNAGE	2789
DIAM.ᵗ OF CYLINDERS	52 & 71
STROKE	60

SCALE ½ = ONE FOOT

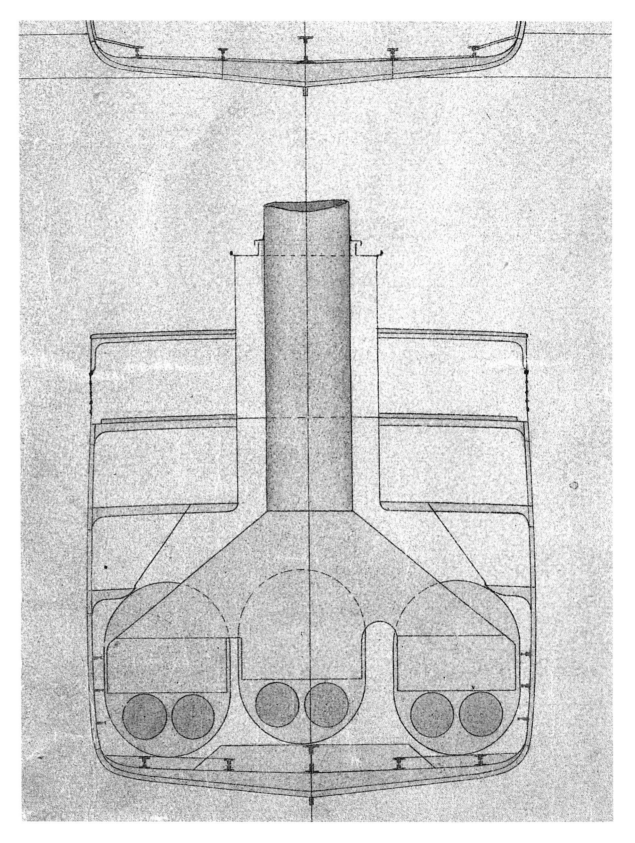

Arabic & Coptic

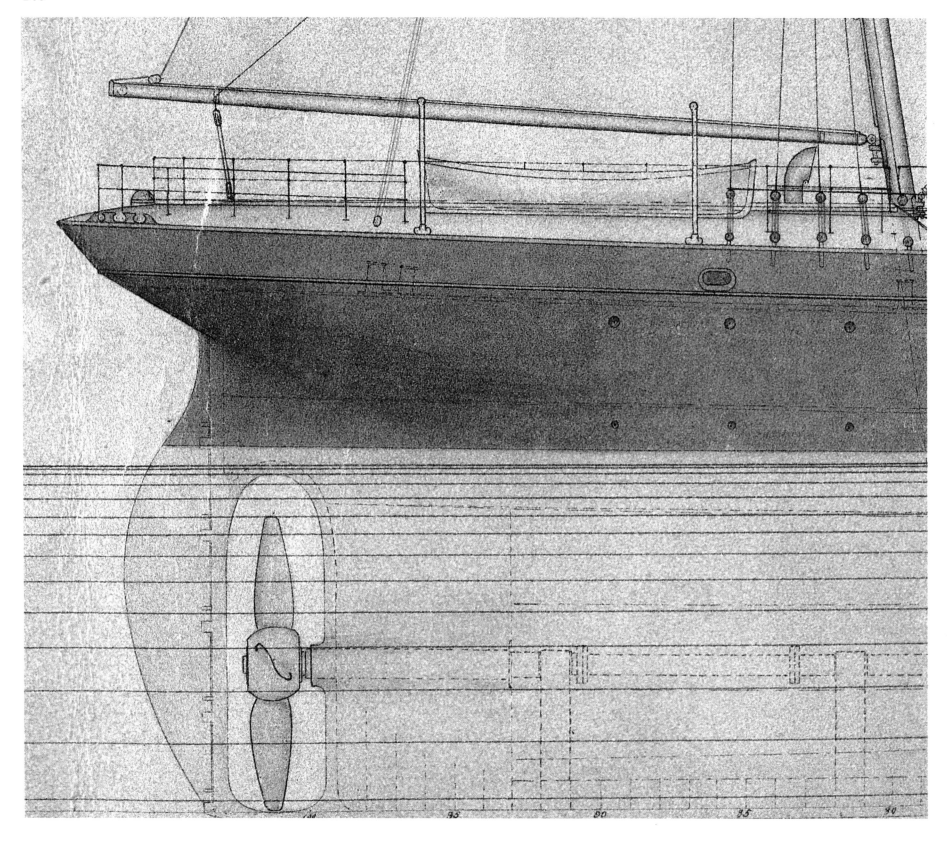

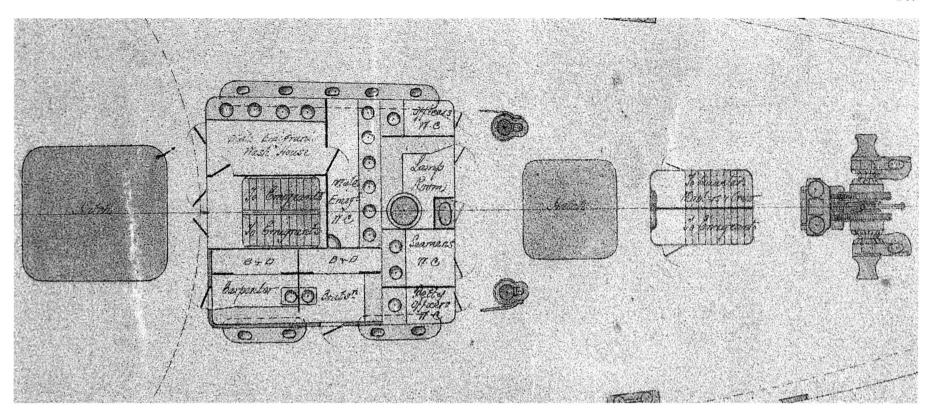

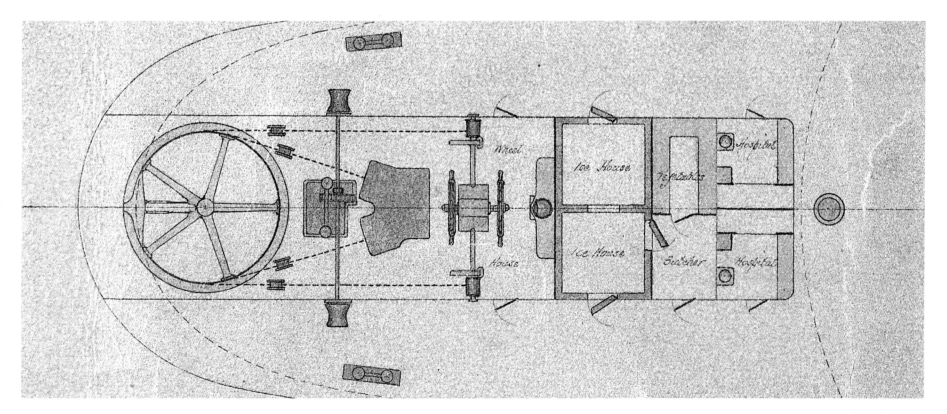

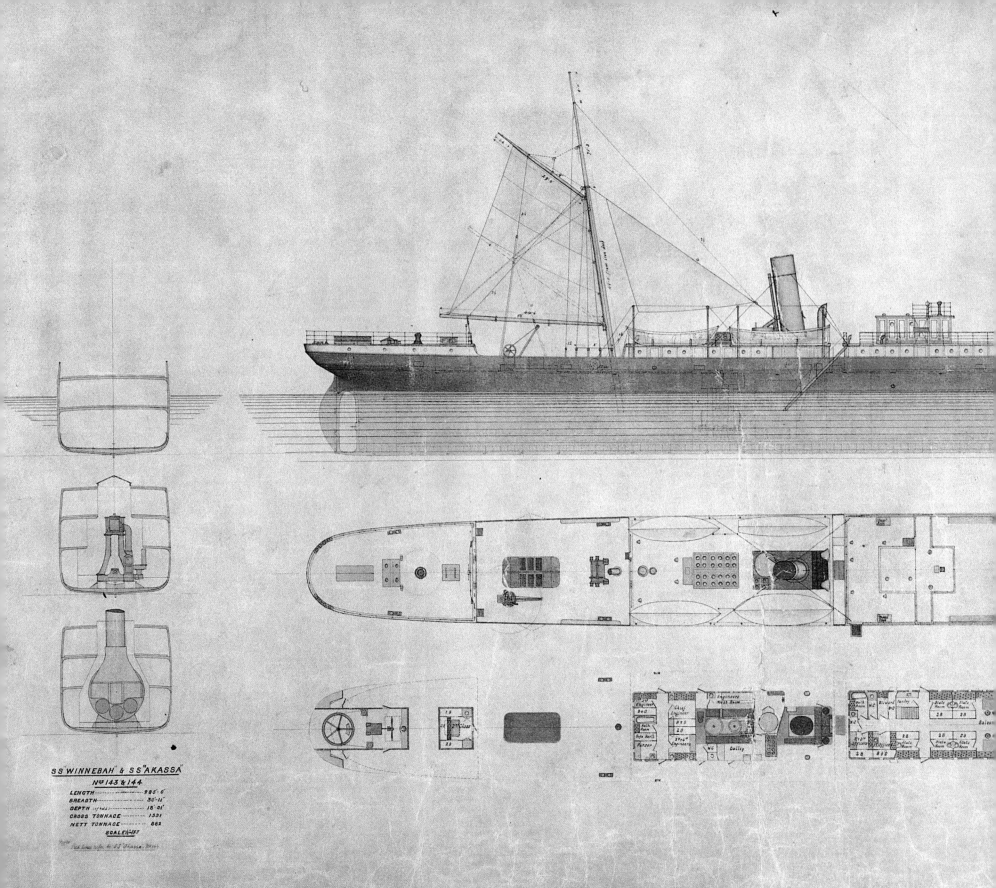

SS "WINNEBAH" & SS "AKASSA"
Nº 143 & 144

LENGTH ------- 235'0"
BREADTH ------- 30'11"
DEPTH (moulded) ------- 16'01"
GROSS TONNAGE ------- 1331
NETT TONNAGE ------- 862

SCALE 4=1FT

Winnebah & Akassa

	Winnebah	*Akassa*
Launched	16 April 1881	24 June 1881
Delivered	1 July 1881	17 August 1881
Yard Numbers	143	144
Owners	The African Steamship Company, London	
Tonnage	1,390	1,389

The construction of these two intermediate class vessels once again saw the involvement of Harland & Wolff in the world of shipowning. The company invested heavily in the Africa Steamship Company with the principal intention of securing the order for these two vessels. Funding for new tonnage was extremely difficult to obtain and, increasingly, shipowners would approach shipbuilders with requests for financial assistance. Faced with the prospect of few, if any, new orders, Harland & Wolff had no option but to acquiesce to these requests.

Neat and functional vessels of 295 feet in length, and operating on a load draught of twelve feet, the *Winnebah* and the *Akassa* were ideally suited to the requirements of the African continent service where many of the ports had limited water depth. Both were powered by a single steam-reciprocating engine which produced a service speed of eleven knots in full load condition. Passenger accommodation was of a high standard, comprising mostly of double and family-cabins, all of which were situated on the main and first intermediate deck. Cargo holds were accessed by twin hatches forward and aft, and each hatch was served by its own cargo winch which could discharge cargo over the starboard side into waiting lighters.

Of steel construction, the hull was immensely strong and light, resulting in a nett tonnage of 882 tons: a remarkable achievement on a gross tonnage measurement of 1,390 tons. Both vessels were operated by their original owner for at least fifteen years, after which *Winnebah* went to Liverpool owners and *Akassa* to Constantinople in 1903. *Winnebah* was demolished in Holland in 1899; *Akassa* met her fate in Genoa in 1912..

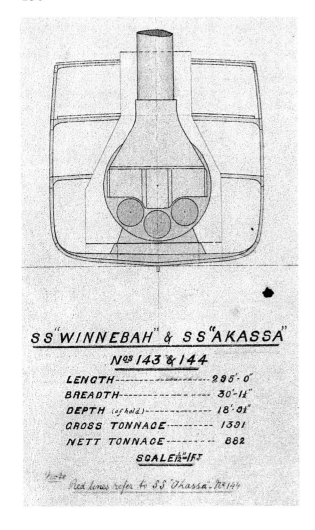

S S "WINNEBAH" & S S "AKASSA"

Nos 143 & 144

LENGTH	285'- 0"
BREADTH	30'- 1½"
DEPTH (of hold)	18'- 9½"
GROSS TONNAGE	1391
NETT TONNAGE	882

SCALE ½"= 1 FT

Note. Red lines refer to S S "Akassa" No 144

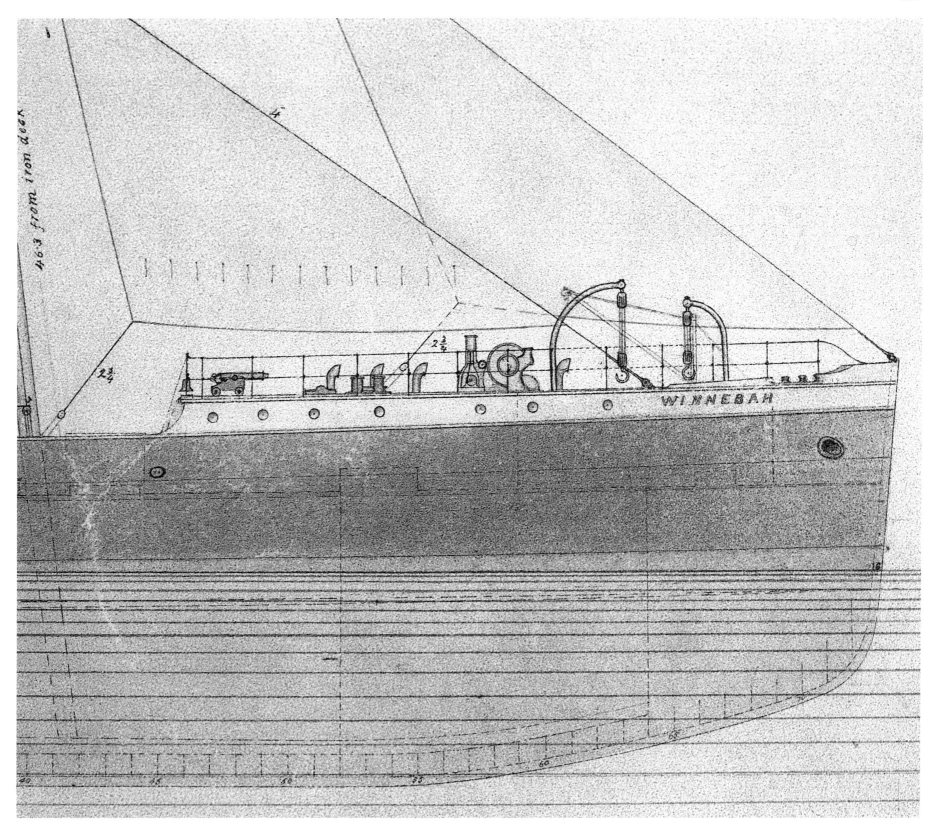

46.3 from iron deck

2 ¾

2 ¾

WINNEBAH

40 45 50 55 60

Winnebah & Akassa

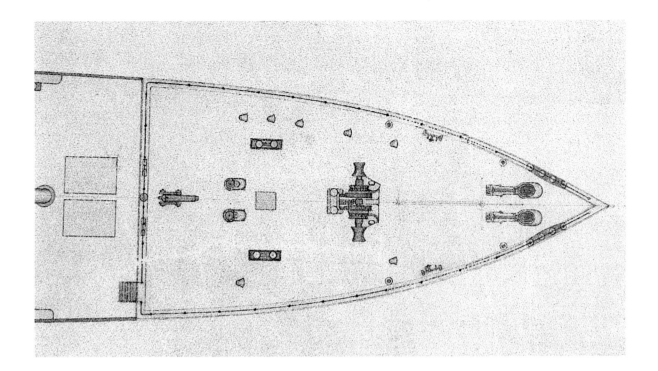

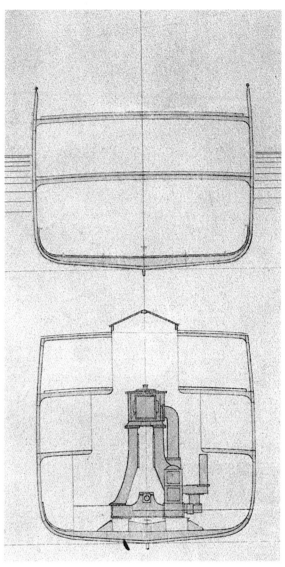

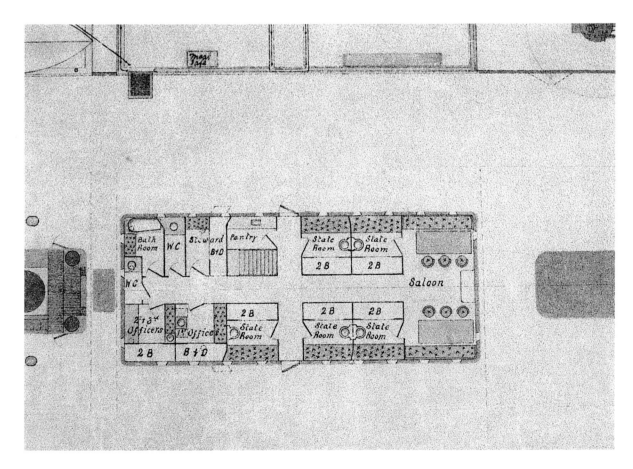

Winnebah & Akassa

Lord Downshire

Launched 29 April 1882	**Owner** Thomas Dixon and Sons,
Delivered 31 May 1882	Belfast
Yard Number 148	**Tonnage** 2,322

By accepting the order for the *Lord Downshire*, Edward Harland returned to his roots in traditional shipbuilding. Constructed once more in iron, rather than the more modern steel, and built as a sailing vessel as opposed to a steamship – to outside observers it appeared that Harland & Wolff was taking a retrograde step. Harland quickly countered such arguments with his own rhetoric, believing that the age of the sailing vessel was not yet over. He pointed out to detractors that sailing ships were much cheaper to construct than steamers and were more economical to operate, particularly over long distances. This may well have been true and his opinions honestly felt, but the *Lord Downshire* would soon come to represent the end of an era in ocean transport – she was eclipsed in the same way that the passenger liner has been made redundant by the advent of the jet airliner.

A beautifully proportioned vessel of three main masts balanced by a stern sail and triple bowsail, the *Lord Downshire* epitomised the elegance and grace of the nineteenth-century merchant sailing ship. Although cargo capacity was extensive, with an unprecedented hold depth of twenty-four feet and nine inches augmented by the absence of an engine, the *Lord Downshire* nevertheless struggled to operate profitably. Passenger accommodation had not been considered in these later sailing vessels and this denied the shipowner an alternative source of income.

It is not then surprising to learn that after only ten years in service the *Lord Downshire* was laid up to await an upturn in the market or another buyer, unfortunately neither was to appear and this magnificent vessel disappeared forever.

— № 148 —
— LORD DOWNSHIRE —
— SCALE ⅛ = 1 FOOT —

LENGTH ----- 292·0
BREADTH ----- 41·0
DEPTH --- HOLD -- 24·9
TONNAGE NETT 2263 GROSS 2322

— № 148 —

— LORD DOWNSHIRE —

— SCALE $\frac{1}{8}$" = 1 FOOT —

LENGTH — — — — 292·0
BREADTH — — — — 41·0
DEPTH — — HOLD — 24·9
TONNAGE NETT 2263 GROSS 2322.

Lord Downshire

54'-0"
13

Lord Downshire

Harland & Wolff Ships 1–150

Name	Delivery Date	Owner	Yard No.
Venetian	14.8.1859	J.Bibby Sons	1
Sicilian	12.11.1859	J.Bibby Sons	2
Syrian	26.3.1860	J.Bibby Sons	3
unnamed	cancelled		4
Jane Porter	1.9.1860	J P Corry	5
Miranda	6.1860	T Yates	6
Grecian	30.1.1861	J Bibby Sons	7
Italian	13.4 1861	J Bibby Sons	8
Egyptian	11.8.1861	J Bibby Sons	9
Ballymurtagh	9.1860	Wicklow Mining	10
Dalmatian	12.1861	J Bibby Sons	11
Arabian	2.5.1862	J Bibby Sons	12
Persian	2.1863	J Bibby Sons	13
Castilian	7.1862	J Bibby Sons	14
Catalonian	2.8.1862	J Bibby Sons	15
Star of Erin	31.10.1862	J P Corry	16
Recife	11.1862	James Napier	17
Worrall	12.1862	J Worrall	18
Alexandra	8.6.1863	T & J Brocklebank	19
Star of Denmark	6.1863	J P Corry & Co.	20
Victoria Nyanza	8.1863	Joshua Prouse	21
Palestine	10.1863	W H Tindall	22
Olano	9.1863	Larrinaga Steamship Co.	23
Star of Scotia	1.1864	J P Corry	24
Kitty of Coleraine	30.10.1863	Lower Bann Steamboat Co.	25
Waipara	11.1863	J Ritchie	26
Baroda	4.1864	T & J Brocklebank	27
Volador	20.4.1864	G Lomer	28
Star of Albion	7.1864	J P Corry	29
Dharwar	9.1864	Iron Ship Co.	30
Douro	21.11.1864	J Bibby Sons	31
British Peer	2.1865	British Shipowners	32
Sesostris	1865	James Moss	33
unnamed	1865	James Moss	34
unnamed	1865	James Moss	35
unnamed	1865	James Moss	36
Pilot	1865		37
Fairy Queen	1865	Rock Ferry Co.	38
Gypsy Queen	1865	Rock Ferry Co.	39
Boyne	9.1865	W H Tindall	40
Annie Sharp	1865	R G Sharp	41
Duddon	1865	New Steam Navigation Co.	42
Guarani	1865	J Dalglish	43
Broughton	1.1868	Ismay, Imrie	44
Candahar	5.1866	T & J Brocklebank	45
Tenasserim	9.1866	T & J Brocklebank	46
Istrian	21.4.1867	J Bibby Sons	47
Iberian	7.1867	J Bibby Sons	48
Illyrian	25.10.1867	J Bibby Sons	49
unnamed	5.7.1867	Belfast Harbour Commissioners	50
Black Diamond	1867	P Evans & Co.	51
Camel Corsanego	1867	M A Corsanego	52
HMS Lynx	12.6.1868	Admiralty	53
Hebe	1868	W & J Phillips	54
Star of Persia	6.1868	J P Corry	55
Woodlawn	1868	S Morland	56
Star of Greece	9.1868	J P Corry	57
Juliet	1.1869	C T Bowring	58
Elaine	31.5.1869	F Lervick	59
Lady Cairns	4.1869	Harland & Wolff	60
unnamed	5.1869	Dublin Harbour	61
unnamed	5.1869	Dublin Harbour	62
unnamed	5.1869	Dublin Harbour	63
unnamed	5.1869	Dublin Harbour	64
unnamed	5.1869	Dublin Harbour	65
unnamed	5.1869	Dublin Harbour	66
Carry	4.1869	William Gossage	67
Bavarian	5.11.1869	J Bibby Sons	68
Historian	9.3.1870	T & J Harrison	69
Bulgarian	20.3.1870	J Bibby Sons	70
Bohemian	29.5.1870	J Bibby Sons	71
unnamed	1870	Lord Erne	72
Oceanic	24.2.1871	Oceanic Steam Navigation Co.	73
Atlantic	3.6.1871	Oceanic Steam Navigation Co.	74
Pacific Baltic	2.9.1871	Oceanic Steam Navigation Co.	75
Republic	21.1.1872	Oceanic Steam Navigation Co.	76
Adriatic	31.3.1872	Oceanic Steam Navigation Co.	77
Camel	17.9.1870	Harland & Wolff	78
Arctic Celtic	17.10.1872	Oceanic Steam Navigation Co.	79
Gaelic	7.1.1873	Oceanic Steam Navigation Co.	80
Belgic	29.3.1873	Oceanic Steam Navigation Co.	81
Star of Germany	20.5.1872	J P Corry	82
Hellenic Britannic	6.6.1874	Oceanic Steam Navigation Co.	83
Ferry No. 1	1.10.1872	Belfast Harbour Commissioners	84
Germanic	24.4.1875	Oceanic Steam Navigation Co.	85
Star of Bengal	7.3.1874	J P Corry	86
Belfast	26.10.1874	T & J Brocklebank	87
Star of Russia	12.2.1875	J P Corry	88
Majestic	24.6.1875	T & J Brocklebank	89
Aglaia	13.4.1875	Workman Brothers	90
East Croft	10.8.1875	J Gambles	91
Connaught Ranger	23.10.1875	J G McCormick	92
Millie	27.7.1875	William Gossage	93
Katie	1875	William Gossage	94
Fiji	29.10.1875	W J Myers	95
Pizarro	20.12.1875	W J Myers	96
unnamed	1875	W Henderson	97
unnamed	1875	W Henderson	98
unnamed	1875	W Henderson	99
Princess Beatrice	4.2.1876	Larne & Stranraer Steam Packet Co.	100
Thursby	16.7.1876	W Thursby	101
unnamed	1876	Cork Harbour Commissioners	102
Lord Cairns	1878	T Dixon Hughes	103
unnamed	1875		104
Mousmie	1876		105
E J Harland	1.6.1876	Samuel Lawther, Thomas Dixon & Sons	106
Thurland Castle	20.9.1876	Lancaster Shipowners	107
Steelfield	1.1.1877	R C McNaughton	108
Gladys	5.1876	N Mathieson	109
Slieve More	24.3 1877	W P Sinclair	110
Slieve Bawn	12.5.1877	W P Sinclair	111
The Lagan	22.2.1876	A Guiness	112
Star of Italy	18.10.1877	J P Corry	113
Star of France	5.1.1878	J P Corry	114
Slieve Roe	16.3.1878	W P Sinclair	115
River Lagan	14.8.1877	R Neill & Sons	116
HMS Hecla	24.8.1878	Admiralty	117
British Empire	10.8.1878	British Shipowners	118
Faugh-a-Ballagh	21.6.1878	Dublin Harbour	119
G W Wolff	25.10.1878	S Lawther	120
Nubia	2.1879	African Steamship	121
Shahjehan	22.2.1879	Asiatic Steam Navigation Co.	122
Shahzada	4.1879	Asiatic Steam Navigation Co.	123
Maharaja	3.5.1879	Asiatic Steam Navigation Co.	124
Maharani	5.6.1879	Asiatic Steam Navigation Co.	125
Fair Head	3.7.1879	Ulster Steamship	126
British Crown	8.10.1879	British Shipowners	127
Galgorm Castle	21.8.1879	A McMullin	128
Lord Dufferin	14.11.1879	T Dixon	129
Dawpool	24.1.1880	North Western Shipping Co.	130
HMS Algerine	12.12.1880	Admiralty	131
Holmhurst	12.12.1879	J H Thursley	132
Winnebah	9.6.1880	Asiatic Steam Navigation Co.	133
Peshwa Rosetta	27.8.1880	Peninsular & Oriental	134
White Head	1880	Ulster Steamship	135
Black Head	14.3.1881	Ulster Steamship	136
British Merchant	25.8.1880	British Shipowners	137
British Queen	15.1.1881	British Shipowners	138
British King	29.3.1881	British Shipowners	139
Woodhopper	1880	Oceanic Steam Navigation Co.	140
Arabic	12.8.1881	Oceanic Steam Navigation Co.	141
Coptic	9.11.1881	Oceanic Steam Navigation Co.	142
Minnehaha Winnebah	1.7.1881	African Steamship	143
Akassa	17.8.1881	African Steamship	144
Shannon	5.1.1882	Peninsular & Oriental	145
Garfield	19.2.1882	North Western Shipping	146
British Prince	4.4.1882	British Shipowners	147
Lord Downshire	31.5.1882	T Dixon	148
Mandingo	6.5.1882	African Steamship	149
Walter H Wilson	18.8.1882	S Lawther	150